FOOD SCIENCE AND

BETA-CAROTENE

FUNCTIONS, HEALTH BENEFITS
AND ADVERSE EFFECTS

FOOD SCIENCE AND TECHNOLOGY

Additional books in this series can be found on Nova's website under the Series tab.

Additional e-books in this series can be found on Nova's website under the e-book tab.

FOOD SCIENCE AND TECHNOLOGY

BETA-CAROTENE

FUNCTIONS, HEALTH BENEFITS AND ADVERSE EFFECTS

MAXIME LEFEVRE
EDITOR

New York

For permission to use material from this book please contact us:
Telephone 631-231-7269; Fax 631-231-8175
Web Site: http://www.novapublishers.com

NOTICE TO THE READER

Library of Congress Cataloging-in-Publication Data

ISBN: 978-1-62417-173-4
Library of Congress Control Number: 2012950968

Published by Nova Science Publishers, Inc. † New York

CONTENTS

PREFACE

In this book, the authors present current research in the study of the functions, health benefits and adverse effects of beta-carotene. Topics include the role of carotenoids and its metabolites in adipocyte biology; B-carotene and peroxisome proliferator-activated receptor gammas; beta-carotene's effects on human health and its applications in food; the different formulations and techniques useful for beta-carotene stabilization and administration; and the effects of dietary beta-carotene on lung function, respiratory symptoms and chronic obstructive pulmonary disease.

Chapter 1 – In recent years, the world has seen an alarming increase in metabolic diseases including obesity, insulin resistance, diabetes, fatty liver disease, and atherosclerosis. Recent studies have clearly identified adipose tissue as a critical site for whole body metabolic regulation via carotenoid metabolism and storage.

A growing body of evidence supports the concept that the bioavailability of dietary carotenoids and their metabolic products (retinoids) not only provide protection against oxidative stress but also act as nuclear regulatory factors interlinking adipocytes, with vitamin A metabolism. These actions include growth and proliferation, regulation of fuel metabolism, adipokine production, and constitute an important component of the endocrine effects of this organ, on systemic carbohydrate and lipid homeostasis.

Several large epidemiological studies have shown a correlation between lower plasma carotenoid levels and increased risk of obesity, metabolic syndrome (MetS), type 2 diabetes (T2DM) and cardiovascular disease (CVD). Food based interventional studies suggest that specifically increased consumption of green leafy vegetables, which are important dietary sources of carotenoids, have been associated with reduced risk for T2DM and CVD.

In contrast, the interpretation of adult carotenoid supplementation trials with supra-physiological doses of single or a few combined vitamins, have been mixed for disease prevention, and may even show detrimental effects.

Consequently, there is a critical need to evaluate the effects of whole food or whole food supplements in the prevention of obesity and its related metabolic dysregulation. In this Chapter, the evidence for a role of carotenoids and its metabolites in adipocyte biology will be evaluated, and the rational for establishing recommended daily intakes and desirable serum and tissue levels, through well designed epidemiological studies, will be proposed.

Chapter 2 – Peroxisome proliferator-activated receptor gamma (PPARγ), a member of the nuclear hormone receptor superfamily, functions as a transcription factor that regulates several biological processes, including growth and differentiation. It has been reported that PPARγ is involved in numerous physiological and pathological processes which β-carotene takes part in, such as antiproliferative action of β-carotene against cancer cells, and the inhibitory effects of β-carotene and its metabolites (vitamin A and its derivatives retinaldehyde and retinoic acid) on differentiation of pre-adipocytes into adipocytes and adiogenesis for the control of body adiposity. β-Carotene-15,15'-monooxygenase (Bcmo1) is the key enzyme for vitamin A production. *Bcmo1*, a PPARγ target gene, is inducedly expressed during adipocyte differentiation and highly expressed in mature adipocytes. Mice deficient in BCMO1 develop dyslipidemia and are susceptible to high fat diet-induced obesity. Dietary β-carotene decreased *PPARr* expression in adipose issue of vitamin A-deficient mice. In addition, PPARγ is also involved in some biological functions of other carotenoids, such as inhibitory effects of lycopene on the proliferation of prostate cancer cells, the anti-obesity effects of astaxanthin, bixin, β-cryptoxanthin, fucoxanthin and its metabolites, lycopene, and neoxanthin, modification of inflammatory responses by lutein and lycopene in macrophages stimulated, and the regulatory effects of lycopene on cholesterol synthesis and efflux in macrophages.

Chapter 3 – The purpose of this chapter is to review the main functions, benefits and possible adverse effects of beta-carotene on human health and its applications in food. More than 600 carotenoids have been identified from vegetable and animal sources, which possess varying levels of pro-vitamin A activity. Carotenoids from vegetables provide approximately 68% of the vitamin A ingested in the diet. According to FAO (2003), approximately 500 million people suffer from the effects of vitamin A deficiency, such as xerophthalmia, and each year three million malnourished people go blind due to insufficient vitamin A. The antioxidant capacity of carotenoids, i.e., ability to prevent peroxidation, is most likely responsible for their ability to protect against the detrimental health effects of vitamin A deficiency. Subclinical vitamin A deficiency, in which visible signs of xerophthalmia are absent, intensifies the severity of certain illnesses, such as diarrhea and other infectious diseases, eventually resulting in immunodeficiency of exclusively nutritional origin. Other roles have also been described for carotenoids in humans, the best known of which is their capacity to be converted into retinols (provitamin A activity). In addition to their function as the macular pigment of the eye, these substances are involved in a series of cellular processes, including the modulation of the inflammatory response, protection against cancer, prevention of cardiovascular diseases and cataracts, and antioxidant activity. The main carotenoids involved in human health are beta-carotene, alpha-carotene, lycopene, lutein, beta-cryptoxanthin and zeaxanthin, which can be found in blood plasma. Except for zeaxanthin, these compounds are easily obtained from foods; beta-carotene is the most abundant in the human diet. However, the absorption and utilization of carotenoids are influenced by several factors, such as the type and physical form of dietary carotenoids, the ingestion of fat, vitamin E and fibers, and the presence of certain diseases and parasite infection. The provitamin A carotenoid *cis*-isomer (*Z*) is converted less readily into vitamin A than is the *trans*-isomer (*E*). Recently, (*all-E*)-beta-carotene was reported to be absorbed preferentially over (9-*Z*)-beta-carotene in humans. Few adverse effects related to the ingestion of supraphysiological doses of beta-carotene have been described. In rats, excess beta-carotene consumption had a positive effect on the control of arterial hypertension that did not affect biological parameters and had no detectable toxic effects. Due to the controlled conversion of beta-carotene into vitamin A, overconsumption does not cause hypervitaminosis A. In fact, the excessive ingestion of beta-carotene usually leads to carotenodermia, a reversible condition that results in an orange color in the skin due to beta-carotene deposition in the outermost layer of the epidermis. Carotenodermia is often observed in patients with hyperlipidemia, diabetes mellitus or hyperthyroidism. Moreover, it was reported that the combination of beta carotene and vitamin A may have had an adverse effect on the incidence of lung cancer and the risk of death from lung cancer, cardiovascular disease, or any other cause in smokers and workers exposed to asbestos.

Chapter 4 – Beta-carotene (β-carotene) has many benefits on health, in particular it can be used to treat skin diseases, several types of cancer, atherosclerosis, macular degeneration or to decrease oxidative stress. This molecule is soluble in aqueous systems and sensitive to oxidation, thus its encapsulation in appropriate drug delivery systems (DDS) might constitute an appropriate mean to preserve its properties, increase the solubility and enhance its physiological potencies. Various formulations have been developed for beta-carotene limiting its exposure to high temperature, light or oxygen. Furthermore, beta-carotene encapsulation can lead to better efficiency allowing smaller administration doses and consequently reducing its potential side effects. The aim of this chapter is to examine the different formulations and techniques useful for beta-carotene stabilization and administration.

Chapter 5 – This chapter reviews the epidemiological evidence on the effects of dietary beta-carotene on lung function, respiratory symptoms, mortality and risk of developing chronic obstructive pulmonary disease (COPD). Published studies are located by searching several electronic databases using the relevant key words. High levels of intake of beta-carotene were found to improve lung function (forced expiratory volume in one second and forced vital capacity) and appeared to have some protective effects against respiratory symptoms such as dyspnea, cough and excessive phlegm. However, no tentative conclusion on the association between dietary beta-carotene and both the risk and mortality of COPD can be drawn. In view of the emerging epidemiological evidence, further clinical and experimental research is required to ascertain the role of beta-carotene on the aetiology of COPD.

In: Beta-Carotene
Editor: Maxime Lefevre

ISBN: 978-1-62417-173-4
© 2013 Nova Science Publishers, Inc.

Chapter 1

CAROTENOIDS AND ADIPOSITY

*J. Atilio Canas**

Mayo Medical School, Department of Pediatric Endocrinology,
Diabetes and Metabolism, Nemours Children's Clinic,
Jacksonville, FL, US

ABSTRACT

In recent years, the world has seen an alarming increase in metabolic diseases including obesity, insulin resistance, diabetes, fatty liver disease, and atherosclerosis. Recent studies have clearly identified adipose tissue as a critical site for whole body metabolic regulation via carotenoid metabolism and storage.

A growing body of evidence supports the concept that the bioavailability of dietary carotenoids and their metabolic products (retinoids) not only provide protection against oxidative stress but also act as nuclear regulatory factors interlinking adipocytes, with vitamin A metabolism. These actions include growth and proliferation, regulation of fuel metabolism, adipokine production, and constitute an important component of the endocrine effects of this organ, on systemic carbohydrate and lipid homeostasis.

Several large epidemiological studies have shown a correlation between lower plasma carotenoid levels and increased risk of obesity, metabolic syndrome (MetS), type 2 diabetes (T2DM) and cardiovascular disease (CVD). Food based interventional studies suggest that

---

*E-mail: jcanas@nemours.org

specifically increased consumption of green leafy vegetables, which are important dietary sources of carotenoids, have been associated with reduced risk for T2DM and CVD.

In contrast, the interpretation of adult carotenoid supplementation trials with supra-physiological doses of single or a few combined vitamins, have been mixed for disease prevention, and may even show detrimental effects.

Consequently, there is a critical need to evaluate the effects of whole food or whole food supplements in the prevention of obesity and its related metabolic dysregulation. In this Chapter, the evidence for a role of carotenoids and its metabolites in adipocyte biology will be evaluated, and the rational for establishing recommended daily intakes and desirable serum and tissue levels, through well designed epidemiological studies, will be proposed.

INTRODUCTION

The U.S. Department of Health and Human Services objectives for Healthy People 2010 [1] and the latest Expert Panel on Integrated Guidelines for Cardiovascular Health and Risk Reduction in Children and Adolescents: Summary Report [2] include a diet high in fruits and vegetables to promote health and favorably change the trajectory for the development of chronic conditions such as obesity, metabolic syndrome (MetS), type 2 diabetes mellitus (T2DM) and cardiovascular disease (CVD). Despite these and other public health recommendations, few children meet the daily recommended intake of fruits and vegetables due to various reasons [3].

Overweight children and adolescents consume less total fruit and vegetables and more fried food than those that are normal weight or at risk for overweight and consequently, have been reported to have lower serum concentrations of serum carotenoids [4].

Correlates of fruit and vegetable intake in 6-11 year olds in the US were assessed using 1999-2002 NHANES data. Among overweight 6-11 year olds the average intake was 0.94 ± 0.05 cup servings of total fruits, 0.41 ± 0.04 cup servings of fruit juice and 1.08 ± 0.04 cup servings of total vegetables, which falls short of the current recommendations from healthy people 2010 [4, 5]. In this context, supplementation of these essential nutrients as an adjuvant to nutritional counseling therapy may be of importance. Interest in carotenoids and human health goes back more than 80 years, when the link between β-carotene and vitamin A was first demonstrated and the dietary importance of β-carotene and other carotenoids as provitamin A was first established.

1. CAROTENOIDS

Carotenoids are C_{40} lipophilic pigments usually red, orange or yellow in color which are produced by photosynthetic organisms and are a main source of vitamin A in humans. They are used extensively as safe, natural colorants for food, feed, and cosmetics. They are known to be essential for growth and differentiation of cells, regulation of fuel metabolism and constitute an important component of the endocrine effect of adipose tissue on systemic carbohydrate and lipid homeostasis. Carotenoid primary dietary sources are fruits and vegetables, though they can also be obtained from bread, eggs, beverages, fats, and oils [6].

In the human diet, there over 40 carotenoids, but only six are ubiquitous in human serum, namely β-carotene, α-carotene, β-cryptoxanthin, lycopene, lutein, and zeaxanthin [6].

2. EFFECTS OF β -CAROTENE AND METABOLITES ON ADIPOSE TISSUE

Adipose tissue has been recognized as the quantitatively most important energy store of the human body, in addition to its functions as mechanical and thermal insulator.

In mammals, the adipose organ is localized in several depots including white as well as brown adipose tissues. The largest depots are found subcutaneously and in the abdominal region. There are no sharp limits between the brown and white adipose tissues, and white areas contain a variable amount of brown adipocytes, and their number varies with age and environmental conditions [7].

Adipose tissue serves as the principal storage site for β-carotene where it plays a crucial role in adipocyte differentiation, adipokine secretion, and lipid metabolism in humans [8, 9].

Carotenoids can be devided into two groups, the carotenes, which are hydrocarbons, and the xanthophylls, which contain oxygen and are therefore more polar than the carotenes. The difference in polarity has consequences on their tissue distribution and also influences repartition and exchange between lipoporoteins. The non-polar carotenes (β-carotene, α-carotene, and lycopene) travel in the core of the VLDL/LDL lipoprotein as opposed to the polar (oxygenated) xanthophylls (β-cryptoxanthin, lutein and zeaxanthine) which are distributed equally between HDL and VLDL/LDL lipoproteins and travel in the outer hydrophilic ring along with partially ionized fatty acids [10-12].

A. Biological Activities of Carotenoid Metabolites

Until recently, the beneficial health effects of carotenoids were attributed to their antioxidant capacity to scavenge free radicals in lipophilic environments such as biomembranes and lipoproteins [13]. However, it is becoming increasingly clear that the various biological effects that carotenoids exert could be driven via a number of different mechanisms. These include direct pro- and antioxidant effects, redox sensitive cell signaling, retinoic acid (RA) signaling pathways through modulation of gene expression via a large family of nuclear receptors and other as yet unidentified mechanisms [14].

A number of intervention trials have failed to show any preventive benefit of carotenoids on disease incidence, and in some cases, long-term supra-physiological dosing has proven to be harmful in people at risk for disease such as smokers [15, 16]. This data are not surprising given the fact that dual pro- and antioxidant effects attributed to carotenoids may be concentration dependent and optimal carotenoid status has not yet been clearly defined in the general population.

The hypothesis that the existence of a "window of benefit" for optimal carotenoid status may only be achieved via appropriate food intake rather than supplementation is corroborated by the number of studies showing benefit with whole food or whole food supplements [9].

Because human adipose tissue represents the main reservoir for β-carotene [8] and adiposity plays a major role in determining disease susceptibility [17], it is conceivable that a putative beneficial effect on health is tightly linked to modulation of the so called "adiposopathy" or "sick fat" phenomena. An understanding of the impact of carotenoid oxidation products and bioactive metabolites in fat metabolism is important in understanding the metabolic effects of carotenoids [18]. β-carotene gains entrance into adipocytes via the class B scavenger receptors (SR-B1 and CD-36) which facilitate uptake of carotenoids from lipoproteins [19, 20] Figure 1.

Increasing evidence suggest that β-carotene derived apocarotenoid signaling molecules can influence adipocyte physiology via high affinity binding to nuclear receptors, the master regulators of adipocyte physiology [21].

B. Enzymatic Cleavage by Carotenoid Oxygenases

In mammals, β-carotene is the natural precursor for apocarotenoid molecules including retinoids (vitamin A and its derivatives) [22]. Adipose tissue expresses two different types of β-carotene metabolizing enzymes, the β-carotene-15-15'-monooxygenase (Bcmo1) which centrally cleaves β-carotene into 2 molecules of *all-trans* retinaldehyde (Rald) and studies in knockout (*Bcmo1$^{-/-}$*) mice show that Bcmo1 is the primary enzyme for retinoid production [23-25].

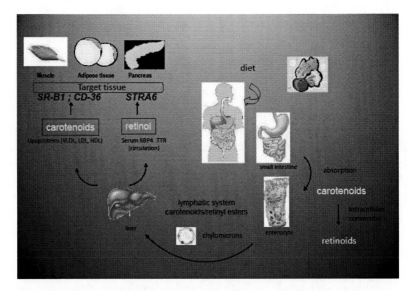

Figure 1. General scheme for the uptake and metabolism of dietary carotenoids and preformed retinoids. Dietary carotenoids, like β-carotene, are taken up into the enterocyte through a process that involves SR-B1. Once inside the enterocyte, β-carotene can be acted upon by the enzymes BCMO1 or BCM02 and either converted to retinal or apocarotenals. The retinal produced from β-carotene cleavage must undergo reduction to retinol or esterified to retinyl esters which can then be packed along with dietary fat and cholesterol into nascent chylomicrons which are secreted into the lymphatic system. Upon entry into the hepatocyte, the retinyl esters undergo rapid hydrolysis back to retinol which is then bound to retinol binding protein 4 (RBP4) and released into the circulation or transferred to the hepatic stellate cells where it is re-esterified and stored in lipid droplets. RBP4 travels in the circulation bound to transthyretin (TTR) to prevent filtration in a 1:1 ratio and reaches target organs where it binds to a membrane receptor STRA6. The carotenoids, retinol and retinyl esters associate with lipoproteins (very low density lipoprotein (VLDL), low density lipoprotein (LDL), and high density lipoprotein (HDL) and retinoic acid (RA) bound to albumin and reach target cells via class B scavenger receptors SR-B1 and CD-36.

The second enzyme is known as β-carotene-9',10'-dioxygenase (Bcdo2) which cleaves β-carotene eccentrically at position 9',10', resulting in the formation of one molecule of β-ionone and one molecule of β-10'-apo-carotenal [26]. (Figure 2) *Bcmo1* gene expression is under the control of PPARγ [27, 28] and is induced during adipocyte differentiation [29]. Rald gets converted to all-*trans*-retinoic acid (*all-trans* RA) which exerts its biological activity by high affinity binding to retinoid acid receptors (RAR) and has been shown to inhibit adipocyte differentiation in cell culture [30, 31].

C. Carotenoid Oxygenases and Apocarotenal Production

A prerequisite for the initiation of vitamin A-dependent and independent physiological processes is the production of biologically active carotenoid metabolites from pro-vitamin A (β-carotene, α-carotene and β-cryptoxanthin) as well as non-provitamin A carotenoids such as lycopene and lutein [18]. The primary β-carotene cleavage product retinaldehyde (Rald), has been shown to inhibit PPARγ signaling, reduce leptin, fatty acid binding protein 4 (FABP4/aP2) and retinol binding protein 4 (RBP4), improve insulin sensitivity and reduce concentrations of fat *in vivo* by inducing oxidative metabolism and lipolysis, resulting in a substantial reduced capacity for fat storage [32]. Alcohol dehydrogenases (ADH's) and short chain dehydrogenase/reductase (RDH's) enzymes reversibly oxidize retinol to retinaldehyde (Rald), and retinaldehyde dehydrogenases (RALDH's) will irreversibly oxidize Rald to *all-trans* retinoic acid (*all-trans* RA), which in conjunction with cellular retinol binding proteins (CRBP's) will determine their intracellular concentrations [33] Figure 2. Intracellular differences in the concentrations of specific retinoid metabolites thus may modulate the various stages of adipocyte differentiation and play a critical part in setting up a favorable nuclear redox signaling mechanism which regulates a variety of cellular functions. Transcription factors, dehydrogenases, kinases and phosphatases, have all been described to be redox regulated in the cell [34].

D. Mouse Studies on the Effects of Carotenoid Metabolites in Adipose Tissue

In mature adipocytes, treatment with pharmacological doses of RA induce lipolysis [35, 36], mitochondrial uncoupling [37, 38], and oxidative metabolism [39, 40] and reduces the production of leptin [41, 42], resistin [43] and RBP4 [44] both in cell culture and mouse models. Surprisingly, high dose supplementation with preformed vitamin A (retinol) does not affect body adiposity in mice [45]. Many of these effects are likely mediated by retinoic acid receptors (RAR's). RAR's are transcription factors that act in conjunction with the retinoid-X-receptors (RXR's) [46] to regulate the expression of numerous target genes in response to RA binding. RXR's are mainly activated by the RA isomer 9-cis Retinoic Acid (9-*cis* RA), whereas RAR's can bind 9-*cis* RA and *all-trans* RA [47]. See Figure 2. Additionally, some effects of RA appear to arise from the activation of PPAR β-δ [36].

There are several studies that indicate an important role for retinoid signaling in adipose tissue physiology, including the observation that *all-trans* RA influences adipocyte differentiation and survival, with high doses inhibiting and low doses promoting adipogenesis of preadipose cells in culture [48]. In addition, the intracellular binding proteins (CRBP I-IV) that mediate the cellular uptake and transport of retinol from the cytoplasm to the nucleus may be associated with adiposity. CRBP-I deficient mice show increased adiposity [49], and CRBP-III-deficient mice have altered lipid metabolism and decreased adiposity [50]. Although CRBP-III was originally identified as a cellular retinol-binding proteins based on the ability of the recombinant protein to bind retinol, a true physiological ligand for CRBPIII has not been identified. It seems possible, even likely, that the actions of CRBP-III in lipid metabolism may involve other ligands than retinol such as fatty acids. Other specific components of the retinoid axis may modulate lipid metabolism and adipogenesis such as the apocarotenal beta-apo-14'-carotenal (apo14), which is the product of asymmetric cleavage of β-carotene by Bcdo2. This apocarotenal has been show to repress PPARγ and RXR activation, inhibiting adipogenesis, even in the presence of the potent PPARγ agonist BRL49653 . In addition apo14 has been shown to suppressed known PPARα responses, including target gene expression and exert an anti-inflammatory effect [51].

$Bcmo1^{-/-}$ animals which abolished Rald production from β-carotene, developed fatty liver and displayed altered serum lipid levels with elevated serum unsterified fatty acids, even on a vitamin A(retinol)-sufficient diet. These mouse mutants were also more susceptible to high fat diet-induced impairments in fatty acid metabolism [23]. Fatty acid oxidase 1 (*ACOX1*) mRNA levels were significantly elevated in $Bcmo1^{-/-}$ mice. Fatty acid synthase (*FASN*) and *SREBP1c* mRNA levels were within the same range. In contrast, levels of steaoryl-CoA-desaturase (*SCD1*) mRNA were significantly decreased in livers of $Bcmo1^{-/-}$ mice.

Analysis of the mRNA levels of PPARγ target genes in visceral adipose tissue revealed that mRNA levels of the fatty acid-binding protein 4 (*FABP4*) and the scavenger receptor *CD36* were significantly elevated in *Bcmo1*$^{-/-}$ mice. Thus, *Bcmo1*$^{-/-}$ mice showed altered mRNA expression of genes involved in fatty acid metabolism in the liver and increased mRNA levels of PPARγ-activated genes in visceral adipose tissues [23].

To further investigate the contribution of Bcmo1 vs. Bcdo2 on adiposity, Amengual et al. recently analyzed the impact of β-carotene supplementation on body adiposity of wild-type and *Bcmo1*$^{-/-}$ mice [52]. In wild-type mice, β-carotene was converted into retinoids. In contrast, *Bcmo1*$^{-/-}$ mice showed increased expression of Bcdo2 in adipocytes and accumulated beta-10'-apocarotenol as the major β-carotene derivative. In wild-type mice, β-carotene significantly reduced body adiposity (by 28%), leptinemia and adipocyte size. Genome wide microarray analysis of inguinal white adipose tissue revealed a generalized decrease of mRNA expression of PPARγ target genes. Consistently, the expression of this key transcription factor for lipogenesis was significantly reduced both at the mRNA and protein levels. Despite beta-10'-apocarotenoid accumulation, this effect of β-carotene was absent in Bcmo1$^{-/-}$ mice, demonstrating that it was dependent on the Bcmo1-mediated production of retinoids [52]. This study underlines the important role of β-carotene for the control of body adiposity in mice and identifies Bcmo1 as critical molecular player for the regulation of PPARγ activity in adipocytes.

E. Effects of Carotenoid Metabolites and Other Signaling Pathways on Insulin Sensitivity

Another important regulator of PPARγ activity is the product of the saturation of all-trans-retinol to produce (R)-all-trans-13,14-dihydroretinol (R-DROL) by retinol saturase (RetSat) [53] Figure 2. Expression of RetSat in adipose tissue is regulated by PPARγ through a PPARγ response element (PPRE) present in the first intron of RetSat [53].

As a consequence, the expression of RetSat is markedly induced during adipocyte differentiation [53]. RetSat is a fibrate/thiazolidinedione-sensitive gene, suggesting that its product R-DROL could be involved in insulin sensitivity.

Indeed, RetSat expression is suppressed in insulin-resistant states, as noted in obese patients and genetically obese (*ob/ob*) mice [53, 54]. RetSat expression was also shown by some studies to be up-regulated and in others suppressed by a high-fat diet in response to mediators of inflammation [53, 55, 56].

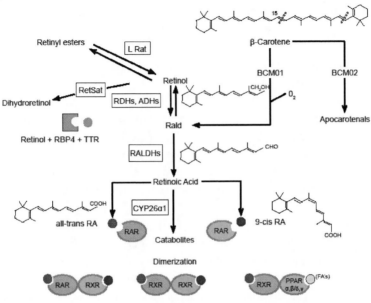

Adapted from Plutzky, G. Circulation Research 2011;108:1002-1016

Figure 2. Intracellular carotenoid and retinoid metabolism. Like certain essential fatty acids, retinol (vitamin A) and its biologically active metabolites retinaldehyde (RALD) and retinoic acids (RAs) cannot be synthesized by higher-order animals but rather must be obtained from the diet either in a preformed state or derived from carotenoids precursors. The retinoid system, with its metabolizing enzymes, intracellular binding proteins (CRBP I-IV), metabolites, and nuclear receptors, each with their own distinct actions and effects, is highly regulated, tightly controlled, and of diverse functional importance. In general, β-carotene is converted to 2 molecules of RALD by the intracellular enzyme Bcmo1. RALD is then converted to retinoic acid (RA) or retinol by retinadehyde dehydrogenases (RDH, RALDHs). *All trans*-RA, present in vivo, activates the retinoic acid receptor (RAR); 9-*cis* RA, which is produced by eccentric cleavage via Bcdo2 has not been demonstrated in vivo, but activates retinoid X receptor (RXR) in vitro. RXR is an obligate heterodimeric partner for PPAR α, β/δ and γ. Despite prior extensive study in areas like adipogenesis, new aspects of retinoid metabolism relevant to obesity, diabetes, and dyslipidemia continue to be identified. Adapted from Plutzky [135].

More important, ablation of RetSat expression by siRNA blocked adipocyte differentiation, while ectopic expression of enzymatically active RetSat enhanced PPARγ activity and adipocyte differentiation in a cell culture model [53]. Mice lacking retinol dehydrogenase 1 ($Rdh1^{-/-}$) activity spare retinol and retinyl esthers, have decreased liver *cyp26A1* mRNA the enzyme that degrades retinol, and grow larger with greater adiposity than WT mice, when restricted in dietary vitamin A [57].

F. Other Animal Studies on the Effects of Carotenoid Metabolites in Adipose Tissue

In contrast to the mouse studies, a recent study in Ferrets looking at the effects of 6-month daily administration of 2 doses of oral β-carotene (0.8 or 3.2 mg/kg/day) in the presence of α-tocopherol and other antioxidant compounds had the opposite effect on body weight, size of body fat and morphometric aspects of subcutaneous (inguinal) white adipose tissues (WAT).

Data showed that at the end of treatment the larger dose induced a 14% higher body weight (P < 0.05) and a significantly higher inguinal fat depot compared with animals treated with the lower dose. In addition, chronic treatment with β-carotene induced a dose-dependent hypertrophy of white adipocytes and increased neoangiogenesis in subcutaneous WAT in all treated ferrets.

Vasculogenesis was independent of adipocyte hypertrophy. There was also evidence of liver steatosis in the ferrets treated with the higher dose of β-carotene [58]. The authors conclude that results differed from preliminary studies performed by the same groups giving the same doses of β-carotene during 3 months but from a different pharmaceutical supplier.

3. ABSORPTION AND METABOLISM

β-carotene absorption in humans depends on three steps: (1) absorption at the enterocyte brush border membrane level via cholesterol transporters SR-B1 and CD36 [59, 60] as well as passive diffusion [61]; (2) enzymatic conversion of a fraction of absorbed β-carotene in a centric fashion by Bcmo1 or eccentric Bcdo2 cleavage [62] with the production of β-10'- apocarotenals via enzymatic oxidation [63] and non-enzymatic oxidation [64, 65]. These processes appears to be species specific with humans absorbing significant amounts of intact β-carotene via chylomicrons [66, 67]; and (3) and via direct secretion of hydrophilic compound such as non-esterified retinol and RA into the bloodstream [68] Figure 1.

A. Intestinal Efficiency in β-Carotene Cleavage and Retinoid Production

Intervention studies with β-carotene in healthy volunteers have lead to the description of a "low responder" phenotype and a "low converter" phenotype. Low responders are individuals who show little variation in plasma β-carotene concentration after acute or chronic supplementation. Low converters on the other hand are individuals that have a low postprandial conversion efficiency of retinol after supplementation, reflected by a low retinyl ester/ β-carotene ratio measured in the chylomicron fraction [69]. Approximately 45% of the western population can be classified as low converters [70, 71]. It has been established that conversion efficiency is depends at least in part on the vitamin A status [72], which is explained by the existence of a negative feedback of RA on Bcmo1 mRNA expression [73, 74].

Retinol/β-carotene ratio variability is reported as high as 221% in some studies and using labeled β-carotene kinetic studies predict that low responders may also display lower conversion efficiency as compared to normal responders [75]. Caution in interpreting these studies is needed because retinol and β-carotene were only measured in plasma and not in the chylomicron subtractions, indicating that non-intestinal lipoprotein fractions were included in the analysis, which contain retinol derived from β-carotene cleaved from tissues such as the liver, and may not reflect absorption alone.

The effects of the food matrix on the bioconversion of provitamin A carotenoids to serum retinol has recently been extensively reviewed including, dietary fat effects, and the effect of genotype on the absorption and metabolism of β-carotene, suggesting that the conversion efficiency of dietary β-carotene to retinol varies widely, in the range of 3.6 to 28:1 by weight [76].

Animal studies propose a diet responsive regulatory network that tightly controls β-carotene absorption, dietary lipid transport and intracellular retinoid production through *all-trans* RA negative feedback regulation of the enzyme Bcmo1. An increase in *all-trans* RA is thought to down regulate intestinal lipid absorption by reducing the expression of the scavenger receptor class B type 1 (SR-BI). *All-trans* retinoic acid via retinoic acid receptors (RAR) induces the expression of the intestinal transcription factor ISX. ISX in turn repressed the expression of SR-B1 and Bcmo1 thus preventing accumulation of excess β-carotene [29].

B. Effects of Body Mass Index (BMI) in Conversion Efficiency Of β-Carotene

An important variable in conversion efficiency may be BMI which has been found to be inversely correlated with conversion efficiency [77], suggesting an interrelationship between β-carotene metabolism and adiposity at least in humans. Many studies report an inverse correlation between BMI and β-carotene levels even after correcting for cholesterol and triglycerides [78-81]. Possible explanations are variable intestinal absorption of ß-carotene, variable conversion of ß-carotene to RALD and RA via the Bcmo1, or accelerated clearance of retinol and ß-carotene due to eccentric metabolism via the Bcdo2 enzyme [9]. The implications for this inter-individual variation are important regarding determination of recommended dietary intake (RDI) for dietary provitamin A intake, especially in vegetarians and obese individuals.

C. Genetic Variation In β-Carotene Absorption and Cleavage

The identification of an individual with a heterozygous (dominant negative) T170M variant of *Bcmo1* displaying carotedermia (hypercaro-tenemia with plasma β-carotene as high as 14.8 µM/L) combined with low serum retinol levels, confirmed the low converter phenotype and triggered investigations into the genetic variations of the *Bcmo1* gene that can affect conversion efficiency. Biochemical characterization of the recombinant T170M *Bcmo1* protein in vitro showed that its activity was ~90% lower than that of the wild type protein suggesting this is a loss of function mutation [82]. Two other polymorphisms occur in the Caucasian population at high frequencies, with allele frequency for the A379V and R267S variant T allele being 24 and 42%, respectively [83]. Effects of the identified mutations were analyzed in vitro, and confirmed in vivo through an intervention study with human volunteers which indicated that women carrying either the *Bcmo1* A379V or R267S+A379V variant alleles had a decreased intestinal β-carotene conversion efficiency with 160% and 240% higher fasting β-carotene concentrations compared to WT carriers [83].

More importantly the conversion efficiency of *Bcmo1* for β-carotene was 32% reduced in carriers of the A379V variant allele and 69% reduced in carriers of the R267S/A379V variant alleles compared to wild type which had a lower inter-individual variation of retinyl palmitate/ β-carotene ratio. Given the high frequency of these SNP's, combined with altered β-carotene metabolism, may account for a substantial part of the low converter trait. Recent findings showing SNP's in genes coding for lipid transporters and lipases are also correlated with plasma carotenoid status brings a much higher level of complexity to interpreting β-carotene levels in the obese population [9]. A recent genome-wide association study in a sample of Italians (n = 1190) identified novel common variants associated with circulating carotenoid levels. Effects were replicated in the Women's Health and Aging Study (n = 615) and in the alpha-Tocopherol, beta-Carotene Cancer Prevention (ATBC) study (n = 2136). In meta-analyses including all three studies, the G allele at rs6564851, near the *Bcmo1* gene, was associated with higher β-carotene (p = 1.6 x 10(-24)) and α-carotene (p = 0.0001) levels and lower lycopene (0.003), zeaxanthin (p = 1.3 x 10(-5)), and lutein (p = 7.3 x 10(-15)) levels, with effect sizes ranging from 0.10-0.28 SDs per allele. Interestingly, these genetic variants had no significant effect on plasma retinol (p > 0.05) and no correlation with BMI was mentioned.

Park et al. demonstrated the T381L in exon 8 of the human *Bcmo1* has a 75% increase catalytic activity for β-carotene [84]. Much more research in this area is needed in view of the number of new non-synonymous SNP's which are being described in the NCBI SNP database (http://www.ncbi.nlm. gov/SNP/) for which currently no data on function or frequency are available [85].

4. β -CAROTENE, ADIPOSITY AND CARDIO-METABOLIC DISEASE

Adiposity is determined by a dynamic equilibrium between food intake and energy expenditure and disruption of this balance leads to obesity and its multiple co-morbidities. Obese individuals with increased risks T2DM, CVD and all-cause mortality are currently classified as having the MetS both in adults [86-91] and children [92, 93].

The clustering of at least 3 conditions including abdominal adiposity, elevated blood pressure, hyperglycemia and two types of dyslipidemia, namely high fasting triglycerides (TG) and low high-density lipoprotein-cholesterol (HDL-C) make up the definition, based on the National Cholesterol Education Program Adult Treatment Panel III (NCEP ATP III) criteria[94, 95].

In childhood, the International Diabetes Federation (IDF) has set similar cut points as in adults, except for measurement of abdominal adiposity which is specific for age, sex and ethnicity [96]. The rising prevalence of obesity and MetS among adults [97] and children [98] in the US constitutes a major public health threat, leading to higher levels of mortality, disability as well as health care costs [99]. The direct and indirect costs to deliver care for cardiovascular disease is approaching $450 billion a year in 2010 and is projected to rise to over $1 trillion a year by 2030, making obesity and MetS a critical medical and societal issue that needs to be addressed [100]. The prevalence of MetS in the US (National Health and Nutrition Examination Survey NHANES 2001–2006) was recently reported at 32.0% among men, 29.5% among women, 6.9% among boys and 3.9% among girls. An inverse relationship between total carotenoids and all MetS components has been reported, even after controlling for total cholesterol and TG among other potential confounders [97, 101]. Total carotenoids were also inversely related to BMI, homeostasis model assessment-insulin resistance (HOMA-IR) and C - reactive protein (hs-CRP) suggesting carotenoids may provide significant anti-inflammatory and insulin sensitizing properties via their interaction in adipose tissue [101].

A. Epidemiological Studies Assessing Carotenoid Status in the General Population

Traditional epidemiological studies that have examined associations between carotenoid exposure/status and health have relied on subjective self reported questionnaire-based data collection. Current research is relying increasingly on laboratory measures to determine exposure more objectively using changes in concentration by HPLC and changes in gene expression with quantitative real-time PCR (nutrigenomics) [102]. In the United States, the best source of data for the descriptive epidemiology of carotenoids comes from a national nutrition survey known as NHANES. There have been several waves of NHANES surveys; NHANES III included both dietary data and biochemical measurements of various plasma carotenoids for a probability sample, selected to create a population sample from which inferences can be made to the overall U.S. population. The dietary intake estimates are based on dietary data obtained from nearly 30,000 Americans, and are therefore robust estimates of intake and are summarized below [103].

These data, compiled by age-specific and sex-specific groupings, are based on a sample size in excess of 20,000 Americans, with all samples analysed in one laboratory [2]. Thus, the NHANES III data are a valuable source of information on typical carotenoid status in a well nourished population.

Table 1. Usual intake of carotenoids (μg/day) from food.
The data are taken from the NHANES III survey (1988-1994),
showing medians (50th percentile) and selected other percentiles

	Carotenoid Percentile		
	10th	50th	90th
β-Carotene	774	1,665	3,580
α-Carotene	2	36	1,184
Lutein + Zeaxanthin	714	1,466	3,021
B-Cryptoxanthine	24	88	319
Lycopene	3,580	8,031	16,833

Data are based on all individuals excluding pregnant and lactating women (n=28,575) and are taken from reference [104].

Table 2. Serum concentrations of carotenoids (μmol/L)
of persons aged 4 years and older.
The data are taken from the NHANES III survey (1988-1994),
showing medians (50th percentile) and selected other percentiles

	Carotenoid Percentile		
	10th	50th	90th
β-Carotene	0.12	0.27	0.63
α-Carotene	0.02	0.06	0.17
Lutein + Zeaxanthin	0.21	0.35	0.61
B-Cryptoxanthine	0.07	0.14	0.35
Lycopene	0.22	0.41	0.67

Data are based on all individuals excluding pregnant and lactating women (n=28,575) and are taken from reference [104].

Carotenoid levels in blood reflect dietary intake, so data for the U.S. may not be an appropriate comparison for countries with different carotenoid intake patterns [103].

B. Human Studies on Cardiovascular Disease and Mortality

In observational studies (case–control or cohort design), people with high intake of antioxidant vitamins by regular diet or as food supplements generally have a lower risk of myocardial infarction and stroke than people who are low-consumers of antioxidant vitamins. In randomized controlled trials (RCT), however, antioxidant vitamins as food supplements have no beneficial effects in the primary prevention of myocardial infarction and stroke [105].

In the United States, the decline in cardiovascular mortality from the end of the 1950s and onwards occurred at the same time as the consumption of fruit and vegetables increased [106]. A high intake of fruits and vegetables, dark green vegetables in particular, have been associated with a reduced risk of MetS [107, 108], T2DM [109] and coronary heart disease [110, 111], stroke [110, 112], and total cardiovascular morbidity [111] or mortality [110, 112, 113]. The European Prospective Investigation into Cancer and Nutrition (EPIC)-Heart study recently assessed the relation between fruit and vegetable intake and risk of mortality from ischemic heart disease (IDH). Participants consuming at least eight servings (80 g each) of fruits and vegetables a day had a 22% lower risk of fatal IHD [relative risk (RR) = 0.78, 95% confidence interval (CI): 0.65–0.95] compared with those consuming fewer than three portions a day. After calibration of fruit and vegetable intake to account for differences in dietary assessment between the participating centers, a one serving (80 g) increment in fruit and vegetable intake was associated with a 4% lower risk of fatal IHD (RR = 0.96, 95% CI: 0.92–1.00, p for trend = 0.033) [114].

C. Human Studies Assessing Effects on Metabolic Syndrome and Type 2 Diabetes

Despite epidemiological studies pointing to an inverse association of serum carotenoids with MetS or T2DM, particularly among adults, RCT's have shown that dietary supplementation with supraphysiologic doses of β-carotene or α-tocopherol had no impact on MetS [115] or T2DM incidence rates [116, 117].

Approximately 5220 adults participated in the SUpplementation en VItamines et Mine´raux AntioXydants (SU.VI.MAX) primary prevention trial and were randomly assigned to receive a supplement containing a combination of antioxidants (120 mg of vitamin C, 30 mg of vitamin E, 6 mg of β-carotene,

20 mg of zinc, and 100 μg of selenium) at nutritional doses or a placebo [115]. Baseline serum antioxidant concentrations of β-carotene and vitamin C, were negatively associated with the risk of MetS; the adjusted odds ratios (and 95% CIs) for the highest compared with the lowest tertile were 0.34 (0.21, 0.53; p for trend = 0.0002) and 0.53 (0.35, 0.80; p for trend = 0.01), respectively. A high concentration of zinc, in the upper part of the normal range, was associated with an increased risk of MetS. AOX supplementation for 7.5 years did not affect the risk of MetS [115] however the authors suggest that it is possible that the positive effect of β-carotene and vitamin C on the risk of MetS was counterbalanced by the negative effect of zinc supplementation. In addition the baseline levels of β-carotene differed between men (0.46 ± 0.30) and women (0.75 ± 0.67) and may have been high enough to indicate that the participants in this study may have had healthier diets and lifestyles than the population at large [115].

The Physicians Health Study randomized a total of 22,071 healthy US male physicians aged 40 to 84 years in a double-blind, placebo-controlled trial, from 1982 to 1995 to 50 mg of β-carotene every other day for 12 years and more than 99% of the participants had complete follow-up. During the follow-up period, 396 incident cases of T2DM in the β-carotene and 402 cases in the placebo group were reported, for a RR of 0.98 (95% CI, 0.85-1.12). When the period of risk was subdivided by years of follow-up, no benefit was observed for any time period or duration of treatment [117].

Similar results were reported in the α-tocopherol, β-carotene Cancer Prevention (ATBC) Study, a double-blind, controlled trial, 29,133 male smokers aged 50–69 years were randomized to receive either α-tocopherol (50mg/day) or β-carotene (20mg/day) or both agents or placebo daily for 5–8 years (median 6.1 years). Neither supplementation significantly affected the incidence of diabetes: the RR was 0.92 (95% CI 0.79–1.07) for participants receiving α-tocopherol compared with non-recipients and 0.99 (95% CI 0.85–1.15) for participants receiving β-carotene compared with non-recipients [116]. In the Physicians Health Study β-carotene concentrations went from 0.56 to 2.24 μmol/L [118] and in the ATBC study the concentrations went from 0.34 to 5.60 μmol/L which are significantly higher than those achieved by diet alone [116, 117].

D. Recent Studies in Young Adults

Adults that increase the intake of fruits and vegetables from 2 servings to 7 servings per day, report doubling (0.34 to 0.52 μmol/L) of the β-carotene concentrations by 2 weeks of intervention [119]. These studies have assessed the potential relationship of increased plasma β-carotene concentrations with mRNA expression values of proinflammatory markers associated with MetS in healthy young adults (50 men/70 women; 20.8 +/- 2.6 years; 22.3 +/- 2.8 kg/m2). The highest tertile of energy-adjusted fruit and vegetable consumption (>660 g/d) was associated with lower plasma concentrations hs-CRP and homocysteine and with lower soluble ICAM-1, Interleukin-1 Receptor- 1, Interleukin-6, TNFalpha and nuclear factor kappaB1(NFkappaB1) gene expression in peripheral blood mononuclear cells (PBMC) (p for trend < 0.05), independently of gender, age, energy intake, physical activity, smoking, body mass index, systolic blood pressure and circulating non-esterified fatty acids [102].

Another recent RCT study from The University of Florida tested the effects of giving a mixture of antioxidants (AOX's) on measures of insulin sensitivity homeostasis model assessment (HOMA-IR) and quantitative insulin sensitivity check index (QUICKI), endothelial adhesion molecules (ICAM-1, vascular adhesion molecule, and endothelial-leukocyte adhesion molecule–1), adiponectin, and oxidative stress (lipid hydroperoxides) in overweight and normal-weight individuals (N = 48, 18-30 years).

Participants received either AOX (vitamin E, 800 IU; vitamin C, 500 mg; β-carotene, 10 mg) or placebo for 8 weeks. The HOMA-IR values were initially higher in the overweight subjects and were lowered with AOX by week 8 (15% reduction, p = .02). Adiponectin increased in both AOX groups. Soluble intercellular adhesion molecule–1 and endothelial-leukocyte adhesion molecule–1 decreased in overweight AOX-treated groups by 6% and 13%, respectively (p < .05).

Plasma lipid hydroperoxides were reduced by 0.31 and 0.70 nmol/mL in the normal-weight and overweight AOX-treated groups, respectively, by week 8 (p < .05). The authors concluded that AOX supplementation moderately lowers HOMA-IR and endothelial adhesion molecule levels in overweight young adults. Unfortunately the authors did not report on baseline or changes in serum concentrations of the AOX supplements [120].

Our recent studies in children suggest that the absorptive capacity of β-carotene when given as a whole food dried encapsulated fruit and vegetable concentrate (FVJC) did not differ significantly between lean and overweight children. Doses of approximately 3.75 mg of β-carotene daily lead to 303 ± 85% increases in the FVJC treated lean group 0.31 (SE 0.04) μmol/L to 1.1 (SE 0.18) μmol/L, which was similar to the 334 ± 57% increases in the overweight group 0.22 (SE 0.03) μmol/L to 0.98 (SE 0.20) μmol/L. However, in the diet group, the % change in β-carotene increased only 23 ± 94% in the lean group 0.27 (SE 0.09) μmol/L to 0.37 (SE 0.09) μmol/L and it decreased -30 ± 57% in the overweight group 0.21 (SE 0.03) μmol/L to 0.14 (SE 0.02) μmol/L following nutritional counseling [81].

The children were given 2 session of standard nutrition counseling by a registered dietician geared towards increasing the intake of fresh fruits and vegetables from 2 serving per day to a goal of 5 servings per day [81]. A serving equated to 1 cup raw vegetables, 1⁄2 cup cooked vegetables, 3⁄4 cup vegetable juice, 1 medium sized whole fruit (for example apple), 1⁄2 cup cooked or canned fruit, or 3⁄4 cup fruit juice [121].

E. Studies Using Mixed Concentrated Fruit and Vegetable Juice Concentrate (FVJC) Products

A number of mixed concentrated FVJC products have been studied, which may help certain individuals improve nutrient status. A recent systematic search of MEDLINE and EMBASE to identify clinical interventions that examined the effect of commercially available concentrated mixed FVJC supplements on cardiovascular disease risk factors has been undertaken [122]. Twenty-two reports, which used commercially available products, were identified. None of the studies reported any serious adverse effects. Overall, daily consumption of FVJC supplements significantly increased serum concentrations of the major antioxidant provitamins and vitamins found in plant foods (β-carotene, vitamins C and E) and folate [122].

In healthy overweight individuals compared with placebo, supplementation with FVJC for 28 days increased concentrations of serum β-carotene by 264% ($P<0.001$) and α-tocopherol by 14% (P<0.01). After crossover of the active group to placebo, β-carotene and α-tocopherol declined via first-order kinetics, with serum half-lives (t1/2) for β-carotene and α-tocopherol determined to be 22.8±3.1 and 4.6±2.3 days, respectively. Depletion rates for β-carotene correlated with adiposity (quartile 1, BMI = 21.96 kg/m2, t1/2 = 17.6 days vs. quartile 4, BMI = 37.87, t1/2 = 26.3 days; p < 0.05) suggesting that the rates of depletion were correlated with the levels of general adiposity [123].

Functional changes, such as reduced serum homocysteine and increased folate in most studies and improved markers of oxidative stress in protein, lipid, and DNA, were reported for most of the products studied [122]. One study measured inflammatory markers (hs-CRP, Monocyte Chemotactic Protein-1, Macrophage Inflammatory Protein 1-beta, and Regulated upon Activation Normal T cell Expressed and Secreted (RANTES protein), superoxide dismutase pre and post supplementation. The study showed Monocyte Chemotactic Protein-1, Macrophage Inflammatory Protein 1-beta, and RANTES levels were significantly reduced and superoxide dismutase and micronutrient levels were significantly increased in subjects consuming FVJC's, relative to placebo [124].

Limitations of the available studies were related to the diversity of studies conducted with respect to design and study population and the variability in the measured outcomes and assays utilized. The authors conclude that mixed FVJC supplements may serve as an efficacious complement for individuals who have difficulty achieving their daily fruit and vegetable intake such as children [122].

Our group recently performed a double blind placebo-controlled study in prepubertal children designed to determine the effects of supplementation with FVJC along with nutritional counseling on serum β-carotene, retinol, RBP4, and adiposity in lean and overweight boys. Changes in serum β-carotene was considered the primary outcome measure and insulin resistance and factors related to subclinical inflammation were studied as secondary outcomes [81]. The study showed that early signs of obesity-related metabolic alterations such as insulin resistance, hyper-triglyceridemia, subclinical inflammation and low lipophilic nutrients were present in overweight children as compared to lean controls even before the onset of puberty. The study also demonstrates an inverse correlation between β-carotene levels and BMI, insulin resistance measured by HOMA-IR, Leptin/Adiponectin ratio and abdominal fat mass. Of note, the increase in β-carotene concentrations in response to the 6-month supplementation of FVJC, along with the nutritional counseling, allowed the overweight cohort to achieve substantial reductions in HOMA-IR after adjusting for percent weight change ($p = 0.014$).

A rapid intravenous glucose tolerance test to measure surrogate markers of insulin secretion such as the acute insulin response (AIR) which is a marker for β-cell function and the glucose disposition index (GDI) which reflects and integrated measure of insulin secretion and insulin sensitivity showed a trend for improvement but no significant differences between supplement and diet after 6 months of treatment. FVJC treatment effect at 6-months compared to placebo increased the GDI (p = 0.037) for all subjects but the significance was lost when the overweight subgroup was analyzed separately.

The authors speculate that several mechanisms may be at play to explain the results. The FVJC supplementation, significantly lowered TG (p = 0.032) in the overweight boys and this may have played an important role in improving insulin sensitivity. They also speculate that an increase in *all-trans* RA by raising β-carotene would lead to down regulation of intestinal lipid absorption by reducing the expression of the SR-BI. *All-trans* RA via retinoic acid receptors (RAR) induces the expression of the intestinal transcription factor ISX. ISX in turn repressed the expression of SR-B1 and Bcmo1 thus preventing accumulation of excess β-carotene [125]. Although *all-trans* RA levels were not measured in this study, a previous intervention study using carrot juice, which is rich in β-carotene, has reported a doubling of plasma *all-trans* RA acid levels without significant increases in serum retinol [126].

Recent studies also suggest that there is a relationship between RBP4, which carries all-trans-retinol to its target tissues and obesity-related insulin resistance in both adults and children [127-130], whereas others have reported conflicting data [131, 132]. Reasons for this dichotomy may involve the failure of most studies to measure vitamin A status (retinol) which is the major determinant of hepatic release of circulating RBP4. RBP4 is produced primarily in the liver, while about 20% is produced in the adipocytes [133]. In the liver, RBP4 secretion is dependent on retinoid availability, such that it is blocked in times of liver retinol deficiency and restored upon repletion [133]. The authors hypothesized that FVJC would have a beneficial effect in lowering the concentration of RPB4 and improving insulin sensitivity. Despite serum retinol being a major biological determinant of RBP4, the study showed no significant treatment effect in lowering RBP4 as a plausible explanation for the improved insulin resistance. After 6 months of treatment the overweight children showed a 1.9% decrease in RBP4 with FVJC as opposed to a 9.5% increase with the placebo, which did not reach statistical significance (p = 0.187). Retinol insufficiency < 1.047 µmol/L was present in 18% of the entire cohort at baseline and 37% at 6 months.

The study showed an indirect correlation between β-carotene and BMI and abdominal fat, and the FVJC overweight treated group had a decrease in the percent change in abdominal fat mass measured by DEXA (p = 0.029) as compared to the diet group. A direct correlation between retinol and abdominal fat mass was seen only at baseline (p = .013), and the significance was lost at 6 months (p = .178). A similar direct correlation between elevated retinol/retinyl esthers and BMI has been observed in cross-sectional studies in both adults and children with increased features of the MetS [97, 101].

In terms of adipokine secretion there was an inverse correlation between β-carotene and the leptin to adiponectin (L/A) ratio (r = -0.596 p = 0.001) which persisted after 3 and 6 months of the intervention. The L/A ratio also directly correlated (p = 0.001) with the abdominal fat mass pre and post intervention. Studies suggest the potential usefulness of the L/A ratio instead of the leptin or adiponectin independently serving as an index of insulin resistance in the adult population [134]. Inverse correlations between the percent change in β-carotene and percent change in leptin (P = 0.01) and percent change in abdominal fat (P = 0.017) confirm the animal studies that suggest that *all-trans* RA derived from centric cleavage of β-carotene, exerts an effect by down-regulation of PPARγ to reduce leptin expression in white and brown adipose tissue [42, 52].

SUMMARY

Although the mechanisms remain unclear, the augmentation of antioxidants such as β-carotene with whole fruit and vegetables or dried encapsulated juice concentrates particularly in children, may exert a potential direct effect on adipocyte biology, by modulating fatty acid metabolism and insulin resistance. The current data also suggests that dietary interventions designed to improve the intake of fruit and vegetables in adults and children call for carefully monitored trials with reliable serum markers of consumption and more sophisticated analyses to uncover mechanistic effects. Measurements of specific fatty acids in addition to lipid soluble vitamins which influence the expression of adipokines such as leptin, resistin or adiponectin and may also play a role by direct interaction with transcription factors, or indirectly via mechanisms linked to fatty acid oxidation, synthesis or storage need to be considered. Because fatty acids are the main components of adipose tissue, it is of essential interest to clarify their biological effects on the expression of relevant adipokines. In this respect, serum β-carotene but not retinol or RBP4, appear to be promising as a potential marker of insulin sensitivity and nutritional status, but additional large-scale studies are needed to validate its usefulness. Research recommendations for full-scale intervention trials to test the preventive potential of vitamin C, vitamin E, selenium, and beta-carotene and other carotenoids for chronic disease will require careful dosing protocols to maintain adequate levels of these important molecules. At the present time, there is no resolution of the possible impact of supplementing these nutrients in healthy vs. obese individuals or as preventive measures for chronic disease.

ABBREVIATIONS

AIR acute insulin response
AOX antioxidants
APO apolipoprotein
Bcmo1 β-carotene-15,15′-monooxygenase
Bcmo2 β-carotene-9′,10′-monooxygenase
BMI body mass index (kg/m^2)
CI confidence interval
CRBPI, -II, and -III cellular retinol-binding protein, type I, -type II and -type III
CVD cardiovascular disease
FABP4/aP2 Fatty acid binding protein 4
FVJC fruit and vegetable juice concentrate
GDI glucose disposition index
GLUT4 glucose transporter 4
HDL high density lipoprotein
HOMA-IR homeostasis model assessment-insulin resistance
HPLC High performance liquid chromatography
HSC hepatic stellate cell
Hs-CRP high sensitivity C-reactive protein
HSL hormone sensitive lipase
ICAM-1 intracellular adhesion molecule- 1
IDH ischemic heart disease
ISX intestine specific homeobox
LDL low density lipoprotein
LPL lipoprotein lipase
LRAT lecithin, retinol acyltransferase
MetS metabolic syndrome
NAFLD non-alcoholic fatty liver disease
NHANES National health and examination survey
PBMC's peripheral blood mononuclear cells
PCR polymerase chain reaction
PPAR peroxisome proliferator-activated receptor α, β/δ, γ
PPRE peroxisome proliferator-activated receptor response elements
QUICKI quantitative insulin sensitivity check index
RA retinoic acid
RALD retinaldehyde

RALDH retinaldehyde dehydrogenase
RANTES Regulated upon Activation Normal T cell Expressed and Secreted
    protein
RAR retinoic acid receptor
RBP4 retinol-binding protein 4
Ret-Sat retinol saturase
RDI recommended dietary intake
RDH retinol dehydrogenase
R-DROL (R)-all-trans-13,14-dihydroretinol
REH retinyl ester hydrolase
RR relative risk
RXR retinoid X receptor
SCD1 stearoyl Co-A desaturase 1
SE standard error
siRNA small inhibitory RNA
SNP single nucleotide polymorphism
SR-B1 scavenger receptor class B, type I
STRA6 stimulated by retinoic acid 6
T2DM Type II Diabetes Mellitus
TNF-alpha tissue necrosis factor alpha
TTR transthyretin
US United States
VLDL very low density lipoprotein
WAT white adipose tissue
WT wild type

REFERENCES

[1]   U.S. Department of Agriculture and U.S. Department of Health and
       Human Services. Dietary Guidelines for Americans, 2010. 7th Edition,
       Washington, DC: U.S. Government Printing Office, December 2010.

[2]   ADOLESCENTS, E.P.O.I.G.F.C.H.A.R.R.I.C.A., Expert Panel on
       Integrated Guidelines for Cardiovascular Health and Risk Reduction in
       Children and Adolescents: Summary Report Pediatrics, 2011: p. *2009-
       2107C*.

[3]   Nebeling, L., et al., Still not enough: can we achieve our goals for
       Americans to eat more fruits and vegetables in the future? *Am. J. Prev.
       Med*, 2007. 32(4): p. 354-5.

[4]   Lorson, B.A., H.R. Melgar-Quinonez, and C.A. Taylor, Correlates of Fruit and Vegetable Intakes in US Children. *Journal of the American Dietetic Association,* 2009. 109(3): p. 474-478.

[5]   DietaryGuidelinesforAmericans,2010,   U.S.D.o.A.a.U.S.D.o.H.a.H. Services, Editor 2010, U.S. Goverment Printing Office: Washington D.C>.

[6]   Rao, A.V. and L.G. Rao, Carotenoids and human health. *Pharmacol. Res,* 2007. 55(3): p. 207-16.

[7]   Cinti, S., Adipocyte differentiation and transdifferentiation: plasticity of the adipose organ. *J. Endocrinol. Invest,* 2002. 25(10): p. 823-35.

[8]   Kaplan, L.A., J.M. Lau, and E.A. Stein, Carotenoid composition, concentrations, and relationships in various human organs. *Clin. Physiol. Biochem,* 1990. 8(1): p. 1-10.

[9]   Tourniaire, F., et al., β-Carotene conversion products and their effects on adipose tissue. *Genes and Nutrition,* 2009. 4(3): p. 179-187.

[10]   Johnson, E.J. and R.M. Russell, Distribution of orally administered beta-carotene among lipoproteins in healthy men. *Am. J. Clin. Nutr,* 1992. 56(1): p. 128-35.

[11]   Schweigert, F.J., et al., Effect of the stage of lactation in humans on carotenoid levels in milk, blood plasma and plasma lipoprotein fractions. *Eur. J. Nutr,* 2004. 43(1): p. 39-44.

[12]   Parker, R.S., Absorption, metabolism, and transport of carotenoids. *FASEB J,* 1996. 10(5): p. 542-51.

[13]   Sies, H., W. Stahl, and A.R. Sundquist, Antioxidant functions of vitamins. Vitamins E and C, beta-carotene, and other carotenoids. *Ann. N Y Acad. Sci,* 1992. 669: p. 7-20.

[14]   Elliott, R., Mechanisms of genomic and non-genomic actions of carotenoids. *Biochim. Biophys. Act*a, 2005. 1740(2): p. 147-54.

[15]   Gallicchio, L., et al., Carotenoids and the risk of developing lung cancer: a systematic review. *The American Journal of Clinical Nutrition,* 2008. 88(2): p. 372-383.

[16]   Greenwald, P., Beta-carotene and lung cancer: a lesson for future chemoprevention investigations? *J. Natl. Cancer Inst,* 2003. 95(1): p. E1.

[17]   Kahn, S.E., R.L. Hull, and K.M. Utzschneider, Mechanisms linking obesity to insulin resistance and type 2 diabetes. *Nature,* 2006. 444(7121): p. 840-6.

[18] Wang, X.-D., Biological Activities of Carotenoid Metabolites.
      Carotenoids, ed. G. Britton. Vol. 5. 2009, Besel, Boston, Berlin:
      Birkhouser Verlag.

[19] Kiefer, C., et al., A class B scavenger receptor mediates the cellular
      uptake of carotenoids in Drosophila. *Proc. Natl. Acad. Sci. U S A*, 2002.
      99(16): p. 10581-6.

[20] Voolstra, O., et al., The Drosophila class B scavenger receptor NinaD-I
      is a cell surface receptor mediating carotenoid transport for visual
      chromophore synthesis. *Biochemistry*, 2006. 45(45): p. 13429-37.

[21] Mangelsdorf, D.J. and R.M. Evans, The RXR heterodimers and orphan
      receptors. *Cell*, 1995. 83(6): p. 841-50.

[22] von Lintig, J., *Colors with functions: elucidating the biochemical and
      molecular basis of carotenoid metabolism. Annu. Rev. Nutr,* 2010. 30: p.
      35-56.

[23] Hessel, S., et al., CMO1 deficiency abolishes vitamin A production from
      beta-carotene and alters lipid metabolism in mice. *J. Biol. Chem*, 2007.
      282(46): p. 33553-61.

[24] Fierce, Y., et al., In vitro and in vivo characterization of retinoid
      synthesis from beta-carotene. *Arch. Biochem. Biophys,* 2008. 472(2): p.
      126-38.

[25] Lindshield, B.L., et al., Lycopene biodistribution is altered in 15,15'-
      carotenoid monooxygenase knockout mice. *J. Nutr*, 2008. 138(12): p.
      2367-71.

[26] Kiefer, C., et al., Identification and characterization of a mammalian
      enzyme catalyzing the asymmetric oxidative cleavage of provitamin A.
      J. Biol. Chem, 2001. 276(17): p. 14110-6.

[27] Boulanger, A., et al., Identification of beta-carotene 15,15andprime;-
      monooxygenase as a peroxisome proliferator-activated receptor target
      gene. *FASEB J.*, 2003: p. 02-0690fje.

[28] Gong, X., et al., Cooperation between MEF2 and PPARgamma in
      human intestinal beta,beta-carotene 15,15'-monooxygenase gene
      expression. *BMC Mol. Biol,* 2006. 7: p. 7.

[29] Lobo, M.V., et al., Localization of the lipid receptors CD36 and CLA-
      1/SR-BI in the human gastrointestinal tract: towards the identification of
      receptors mediating the intestinal absorption of dietary lipids. *J.
      Histochem. Cytochem*, 2001. 49(10): p. 1253-60.

[30] Kuri-Harcuch, W., Differentiation of 3T3-F442A cells into adipocytes is
      inhibited by retinoic acid. *Differentiation*, 1982. 23(2): p. 164-9.

[31] Schwarz, E.J., et al., Retinoic acid blocks adipogenesis by inhibiting C/EBPbeta-mediated transcription. *Mol. Cell Biol,* 1997. 17(3): p. 1552-61.

[32] Ziouzenkova, O., et al., Retinaldehyde represses adipogenesis and diet-induced obesity. *Nat. Med,* 2007. 13(6): p. 695-702.

[33] Duester, G., F.A. Mic, and A. Molotkov, Cytosolic retinoid dehydrogenases govern ubiquitous metabolism of retinol to retinaldehyde followed by tissue-specific metabolism to retinoic acid. *Chem. Biol. Interact,* 2003. 143-144: p. 201-10.

[34] Lukosz, M., et al., Nuclear redox signaling. *Antioxid. Redox. Signal,* 2010. 12(6): p. 713-42.

[35] Ribot, J., et al., Changes of Adiposity in Response to Vitamin A Status Correlate with Changes of PPAR[gamma]2 Expression. *Obesity,* 2001. 9(8): p. 500-509.

[36] Berry, D.C. and N. Noy, All-trans-retinoic acid represses obesity and insulin resistance by activating both peroxisome proliferation-activated receptor beta/delta and retinoic acid receptor. *Mol. Cell Biol,* 2009. 29(12): p. 3286-96.

[37] Alvarez, R., et al., A novel regulatory pathway of brown fat thermogenesis. Retinoic acid is a transcriptional activator of the mitochondrial uncoupling protein gene. *J. Biol. Chem,* 1995. 270(10): p. 5666-73.

[38] Puigserver, P., et al., In vitro and in vivo induction of brown adipocyte uncoupling protein (thermogenin) by retinoic acid. *Biochem. J,* 1996. 317 (Pt 3): p. 827-33.

[39] Mercader, J., et al., Remodeling of white adipose tissue after retinoic acid administration in mice. *Endocrinology,* 2006. 147(11): p. 5325-32.

[40] Mercader, J., et al., All-trans retinoic acid increases oxidative metabolism in mature adipocytes. *Cell Physiol. Biochem,* 2007. 20(6): p. 1061-72.

[41] Hollung, K., et al., Tissue-specific regulation of leptin expression and secretion by all-trans retinoic acid. *J. Cell Biochem,* 2004. 92(2): p. 307-15.

[42] Felipe, F., et al., Effects of retinoic acid administration and dietary vitamin A supplementation on leptin expression in mice: lack of correlation with changes of adipose tissue mass and food intake. *Biochim. Biophys. Acta,* 2005. 1740(2): p. 258-65.

[43] Felipe, F., et al., Modulation of resistin expression by retinoic acid and vitamin A status. *Diabetes,* 2004. 53(4): p. 882-9.

[44] Mercader, J., et al., All-trans retinoic acid decreases murine adipose retinol binding protein 4 production. *Cell Physiol. Biochem,* 2008. 22(1-4): p. 363-72.

[45] Felipe, F., et al., Up-regulation of muscle uncoupling protein 3 gene expression in mice following high fat diet, dietary vitamin A supplementation and acute retinoic acid-treatment. *Int. J. Obes. Relat.*

[46] Petkovich, M., et al., A human retinoic acid receptor which belongs to the family of nuclear receptors. *Nature,* 1987. 330(6147): p. 444-50.

[47] Allenby, G., et al., Retinoic acid receptors and retinoid X receptors: interactions with endogenous retinoic acids. *Proc. Natl. Acad. Sci. U S A,* 1993. 90(1): p. 30-4.

[48] Bonet, M.L., et al., *Vitamin A and the regulation of fat reserves. Cell Mol. Life Sci*, 2003. 60(7): p. 1311-21.

[49] Zizola, C.F., et al., *Cellular retinol-binding protein type I (CRBP-I) regulates adipogenesis. Mol. Cell Biol,* 2010. 30(14): p. 3412-20.

[50] Zizola, C.F., G.J. Schwartz, and S. Vogel, *Cellular retinol-binding protein type III is a PPARgamma target gene and plays a role in lipid metabolism. Am. J. Physiol. Endocrinol. Metab*, 2008. 295(6): p. E1358-68.

[51] Ziouzenkova, O., et al., Asymmetric cleavage of beta-carotene yields a transcriptional repressor of retinoid X receptor and peroxisome proliferator-activated receptor responses. *Mol. Endocrinol,* 2007. 21(1): p. 77-88.

[52] Amengual, J., et al., Beta-Carotene Reduces Body Adiposity of Mice via BCMO1. *PLoS ONE*, 2011. 6(6): p. e20644.

[53] Moise, A.R., et al., Increased adiposity in the retinol saturase-knockout mouse. *FASEB J,* 2010. 24(4): p. 1261-70.

[54] Schupp, M., et al., Retinol saturase promotes adipogenesis and is downregulated in obesity. *Proc. Natl. Acad. Sci. U S A,* 2009. 106(4): p. 1105-10.

[55] Lopez, I.P., et al., Gene expression changes in rat white adipose tissue after a high-fat diet determined by differential display. *Biochem. Biophys. Res. Commun,* 2004. 318(1): p. 234-9.

[56] Lopez, I.P., et al., High-fat feeding period affects gene expression in rat white adipose tissue. *Mol. Cell Biochem,* 2005. 275(1-2): p. 109-15.

[57] Zhang, M., et al., Altered vitamin A homeostasis and increased size and adiposity in the rdh1-null mouse. *FASEB J,* 2007. 21(11): p. 2886-96.

[58] Murano, I., et al., Morphology of ferret subcutaneous adipose tissue after 6-month daily supplementation with oral beta-carotene. *Biochimica et*

Biophysica Acta (BBA) - Molecular Basis of Disease, 2005. 1740(2): p. 305-312.

[59] During, A., H.D. Dawson, and E.H. Harrison, Carotenoid transport is decreased and expression of the lipid transporters SR-BI, NPC1L1, and ABCA1 is downregulated in Caco-2 cells treated with ezetimibe. *J. Nutr,* 2005. 135(10): p. 2305-12.

[60] van Bennekum, A., et al., Class B scavenger receptor-mediated intestinal absorption of dietary beta-carotene and cholesterol. *Biochemistry,* 2005. 44(11): p. 4517-25.

[61] Yonekura, L. and A. Nagao, Intestinal absorption of dietary carotenoids. *Mol. Nutr. Food Res,* 2007. 51(1): p. 107-15.

[62] von Lintig, J., et al., Towards a better understanding of carotenoid metabolism in animals. *Biochimica et Biophysica Acta (BBA) - Molecular Basis of Disease,* 2005. 1740(2): p. 122-131.

[63] Wang, X.D., et al., Retinoic acid can be produced from excentric cleavage of beta-carotene in human intestinal mucosa. *Arch. Biochem. Biophys,* 1992. 293(2): p. 298-304.

[64] Yeum, K.J., et al., The effect of alpha-tocopherol on the oxidative cleavage of beta-carotene. *Free Radic. Biol. Med,* 2000. 29(2): p. 105-14.

[65] Yeum, K.J., et al., Similar metabolites formed from beta-carotene by human gastric mucosal homogenates, lipoxygenase, or linoleic acid hydroperoxide. *Arch. Biochem. Biophys,* 1995. 321(1): p. 167-74.

[66] Wang, X.D., Review: absorption and metabolism of beta-carotene. *J. Am. Coll. Nutr,* 1994. 13(4): p. 314-25.

[67] Borel, P., et al., [Recent knowledge about intestinal absorption and cleavage of carotenoids]. *Ann. Biol. Clin.* (Paris), 2005. 63(2): p. 165-77.

[68] Harrison, E.H., Mechanisms involved in the intestinal absorption of dietary vitamin A and provitamin A carotenoids. Biochimica et *Biophysica Acta (BBA) - Molecular and Cell Biology of Lipids,* 2012. 1821(1): p. 70-77.

[69] Borel, P., et al., Low and high responders to pharmacological doses of Î²-carotene: proportion in the population, mechanisms involved and consequences on Î²-carotene metabolism. *Journal of Lipid Research,* 1998. 39(11): p. 2250-2260.

[70] Hickenbottom, S.J., et al., Variability in conversion of beta-carotene to vitamin A in men as measured by using a double-tracer study design. *Am. J. Clin. Nutr,* 2002. 75(5): p. 900-7.

[71]   Lin, Y., et al., Variability of the conversion of beta-carotene to vitamin A in women measured by using a double-tracer study design. *Am. J. Clin. Nutr*, 2000. 71(6): p. 1545-54.

[72]   Ribaya-Mercado, J.D., et al., Bioconversion of plant carotenoids to vitamin A in Filipino school-aged children varies inversely with vitamin A status. *Am. J. Clin. Nutr*, 2000. 72(2): p. 455-65.

[73]   Bachmann, H., et al., Feedback regulation of beta,beta-carotene 15,15'-monooxygenase by retinoic acid in rats and chickens. *J. Nutr*, 2002. 132(12): p. 3616-22.

[74]   Takitani, K., et al., Molecular cloning of the rat beta-carotene 15,15'-monooxygenase gene and its regulation by retinoic acid. *Eur. J. Nutr*, 2006. 45(6): p. 320-6.

[75]   Wang, Z., et al., beta-Carotene-vitamin A equivalence in Chinese adults assessed by an isotope dilution technique. *Br. J. Nutr*, 2004. 91(1): p. 121-31.

[76]   Tang, G., Bioconversion of dietary provitamin A carotenoids to vitamin A in humans. *The American Journal of Clinical Nutrition*, 2010. 91(5): p. 1468S-1473S.

[77]   Tang, G., et al., Short-term (intestinal) and long-term (postintestinal) conversion of beta-carotene to retinol in adults as assessed by a stable-isotope reference method. *Am. J. Clin. Nutr*, 2003. 78(2): p. 259-66.

[78]   Moor de Burgos, A., M. Wartanowicz, and S. Ziemlanski, Blood vitamin and lipid levels in overweight and obese women. *Eur. J. Clin. Nutr*, 1992. 46(11): p. 803-8.

[79]   Decsi, T., D. Molnar, and B. Koletzko, Reduced plasma concentrations of alpha-tocopherol and beta-carotene in obese boys. *J. Pediatr*, 1997. 130(4): p. 653-655.

[80]   Andersen, L.F., et al., Longitudinal associations between body mass index and serum carotenoids: the CARDIA study. *Br. J. Nutr*, 2006. 95(2): p. 358-65.

[81]   Canas, J.A., et al., Insulin Resistance and Adiposity in Relation to Serum beta-Carotene Levels. *J. Pediatr*, 2012. 161(1): p. 58-64 e2.

[82]   Lindqvist, A., et al., Loss-of-function mutation in carotenoid 15,15'-monooxygenase identified in a patient with hypercarotenemia and hypovitaminosis A. *J. Nutr*, 2007. 137(11): p. 2346-50.

[83]   Leung, W.C., et al., Two common single nucleotide polymorphisms in the gene encoding {beta}-carotene 15,15'-monoxygenase alter {beta}-carotene metabolism in female volunteers. *FASEB J.*, 2009. 23(4): p. 1041-1053.

[84] Park, C.S., et al., Utilization of the recombinant human beta-carotene-15,15'-monooxygenase gene in Escherichia coli and mammalian cells. *Biotechnol. Lett*, 2008. 30(4): p. 735-41.

[85] Lietz, G., J. Lange, and G. Rimbach, Molecular and dietary regulation of [beta],[beta]-carotene 15,15'-monooxygenase 1 (BCMO1). *Archives of Biochemistry and Biophysics*, 2010. 502(1): p. 8-16.

[86] Isomaa, B., et al., Cardiovascular morbidity and mortality associated with the metabolic syndrome. *Diabetes Care*, 2001. 24(4): p. 683-9.

[87] Trevisan, M., et al., Syndrome X and mortality: a population-based study. Risk Factor and Life Expectancy Research Group. *Am. J. Epidemiol*, 1998. 148(10): p. 958-66.

[88] Wilson, P.W., et al., Clustering of metabolic factors and coronary heart disease. *Arch. Intern Med*, 1999. 159(10): p. 1104-9.

[89] Haffner, S.M., et al., Prospective analysis of the insulin-resistance syndrome (syndrome X). *Diabetes*, 1992. 41(6): p. 715-22.

[90] Lakka, H.M., et al., The metabolic syndrome and total and cardiovascular disease mortality in middle-aged men. *JAMA*, 2002. 288(21): p. 2709-16.

[91] Hu, G., et al., Prevalence of the metabolic syndrome and its relation to all-cause and cardiovascular mortality in nondiabetic European men and women. *Arch. Intern Med*, 2004. 164(10): p. 1066-76.

[92] Engeland, A., et al., Obesity in adolescence and adulthood and the risk of adult mortality. *Epidemiology*, 2004. 15(1): p. 79-85.

[93] Biro, F.M. and M. Wien, Childhood obesity and adult morbidities. *Am. J. Clin. Nutr*, 2010. 91(5): p. 1499S-1505S.

[94] Meigs, J.B., Epidemiology of the metabolic syndrome, *2002. Am. J. Manag. Care*, 2002. 8(11 Suppl): p. S283-92; quiz S293-6.

[95] Grundy, S.M., et al., Diagnosis and management of the metabolic syndrome: an American Heart Association/National Heart, Lung, and Blood Institute Scientific Statement. *Circulation*, 2005. 112(17): p. 2735-52.

[96] Alberti, G., Zimmet, P., Kaufman, F., Tajima, N., Silink, M., Arslanian, S., Wong, G., Bennett, P., Shaw, J., Caprio, S., The IDF consensus definition of the metabolic syndrome in children and adolescents, 2007, International Diabetes Federation: Brussels, Belgium.

[97] Beydoun, M.A., et al., Serum Antioxidant Status Is Associated with Metabolic Syndrome among U.S. Adults in Recent National Surveys. *J. Nutr*, 2011. 141(5): p. 903-13.

[98] Ogden, C.L., et al., Prevalence of high body mass index in US children
      and adolescents, 2007-2008. *JAMA*, 2010. 303(3): p. 242-9.
[99] Wang, Y. and M.A. Beydoun, The obesity epidemic in the United
      States--gender, age, socioeconomic, racial/ethnic, and geographic
      characteristics: a systematic review and meta-regression analysis.
      Epidemiol. Rev, 2007. 29: p. 6-28.
[100] Weintraub, W.S., et al., Value of primordial and primary prevention for
      cardiovascular disease: a policy statement from the American Heart
      Association. *Circulation*, 2011. 124(8): p. 967-90.
[101] Beydoun, M.A.C., J.A.; Beydoun, H.A.; Chen, X.; Shroff, M.R.;
      Zonderman, A.B., Serum antioxidant concentrations and metabolic
      syndrome are associated among US adolescents in recent national
      surveys. *J. Nutr.*, 2012.
[102] Hermsdorff, H.H., et al., Fruit and vegetable consumption and
      proinflammatory gene expression from peripheral blood mononuclear
      cells in young adults: a translational study. *Nutr. Metab.* (Lond), 2010. 7:
      p. 42.
[103] Mayne, S.T.W., Margaret E.; Cartmel, Brenda, Epidemiology and
      Intervention Trials. Carotenoids, ed. G.L.-J.S.P. Britton, H. Vol. 5. 2009,
      Basel,Boston, Berlin: Birkhouser Verlag.
[104] Dietary Reference Intakes for Vitamin C, Vitamin E, Selenium and
      Carotenoids., 2000, National Academy of Sciences, Institute of
      Medicine, Food and Nutrition Board, Panel on Micronutrients:
      Washington, DC.
[105] Asplund, K., Antioxidant vitamins in the prevention of cardiovascular
      disease: a systematic review. *J. Intern Med*, 2002. 251(5): p. 372-92.
[106] Verlangieri, A.J., et al., Fruit and vegetable consumption and
      cardiovascular mortality. *Med. Hypotheses,* 1985. 16(1): p. 7-15.
[107] Aeberli, I., et al., Diet determines features of the metabolic syndrome in
      6- to 14-year-old children. *Int. J. Vitam. Nutr. Res,* 2009. 79(1): p. 14-
      23.
[108] Sluijs, I., et al., Dietary carotenoid intake is associated with lower
      prevalence of metabolic syndrome in middle-aged and elderly men. *J.
      Nutr*, 2009. 139(5): p. 987-92.
[109] Carter, P., et al., Fruit and vegetable intake and incidence of type 2
      diabetes mellitus: systematic review and meta-analysis. *BMJ*, 2010. 341:
      p. c4229.

[110] Key, T.J., et al., Dietary habits and mortality in 11,000 vegetarians and health conscious people: results of a 17 year follow up. *BMJ*, 1996. 313(7060): p. 775-9.

[111] Bazzano, L.A., et al., *Legume consumption and risk of coronary heart disease in US men and women: NHANES I Epidemiologic Follow-up Study. Arch. Intern Med*, 2001. 161(21): p. 2573-8.

[112] Gillman, M.W., et al., Protective effect of fruits and vegetables on development of stroke in men. *JAMA*, 1995. 273(14): p. 1113-7.

[113] Strandhagen, E., et al., High fruit intake may reduce mortality among middle-aged and elderly men. The Study of Men Born in 1913. *Eur. J. Clin. Nutr*, 2000. 54(4): p. 337-41.

[114] Crowe, F.L., et al., Fruit and vegetable intake and mortality from ischaemic heart disease: results from the European Prospective Investigation into Cancer and Nutrition (EPIC)-Heart study. *Eur. Heart J*, 2011. 32(10): p. 1235-43.

[115] Czernichow, S., et al., *Effects of long-term antioxidant supplementation and association of serum antioxidant concentrations with risk of metabolic syndrome in adults. Am. J. Clin. Nutr*, 2009. 90(2): p. 329-35.

[116] Kataja-Tuomola, M., et al., Effect of alpha-tocopherol and beta-carotene supplementation on the incidence of type 2 diabetes. *Diabetologia*, 2008. 51(1): p. 47-53.

[117] Liu, S., et al., Long-term beta-carotene supplementation and risk of type 2 diabetes mellitus: a randomized controlled trial. *Jama*, 1999. 282(11): p. 1073-5.

[118] Satterfield, S., et al., Biochemical markers of compliance in the Physicians' Health Study. *Am. J. Prev. Med*, 1990. 6(5): p. 290-4.

[119] Zino, S., et al., *Randomised controlled trial of effect of fruit and vegetable consumption on plasma concentrations of lipids and antioxidants*. BMJ, 1997. 314(7097): p. 1787-91.

[120] Vincent, H.K., et al., Effects of antioxidant supplementation on insulin sensitivity, endothelial adhesion molecules, and oxidative stress in normal-weight and overweight young adults. *Metabolism*, 2009. 58(2): p. 254-262.

[121] Stevens, J., et al., Accuracy of current, 4-year, and 28-year self-reported body weight in an elderly population. *Am. J. Epidemiol*, 1990. 132(6): p. 1156-63.

[122] Esfahani, A., et al., Health effects of mixed fruit and vegetable concentrates: a systematic review of the clinical interventions. *J. Am. Coll. Nutr*, 2011. 30(5): p. 285-94.

[123] Wise, J.A., et al., Î²-Carotene and Î±-tocopherol in healthy overweight adults; depletion kinetics are correlated with adiposity. *International Journal of Food Sciences and Nutrition*, 2009. 60(s3): p. 65-75.

[124] Jin, Y., et al., Systemic inflammatory load in humans is suppressed by consumption of two formulations of dried, encapsulated juice concentrate. *Mol. Nutr. Food Res,* 2010. 54(10): p. 1506-14.

[125] Lobo, G.P., et al., ISX is a retinoic acid-sensitive gatekeeper that controls intestinal beta,beta-carotene absorption and vitamin A production. *FASEB J*, 2010. 24(6): p. 1656-66.

[126] Ruhl, R., A. Bub, and B. Watzl, Modulation of plasma all-trans retinoic acid concentrations by the consumption of carotenoid-rich vegetables. *Nutrition*, 2008. 24(11-12): p. 1224-6.

[127] Graham, T.E., et al., Retinol-binding protein 4 and insulin resistance in lean, obese, and diabetic subjects. *N. Engl. J. Med*, 2006. 354(24): p. 2552-2563.

[128] Balagopal, P., et al., Reduction of elevated serum retinol binding protein in obese children by lifestyle intervention: association with subclinical inflammation. *J. Clin. Endocrinol. Metab,* 2007. 92(5): p. 1971-1974.

[129] Aeberli, I., et al., Serum retinol-binding protein 4 concentration and its ratio to serum retinol are associated with obesity and metabolic syndrome components in children. *J. Clin. Endocrinol. Metab*, 2007. 92(11): p. 4359-65.

[130] Reinehr, T., B. Stoffel-Wagner, and C.L. Roth, Retinol-binding protein 4 and its relation to insulin resistance in obese children before and after weight loss. *J. Clin. Endocrinol. Metab*, 2008. 93(6): p. 2287-2293.

[131] Janke, J., et al., Retinol-Binding Protein 4 in Human Obesity. *Diabetes*, 2006. 55(10): p. 2805-2810.

[132] Ulgen, F., et al., Association of serum levels of retinol-binding protein 4 with male sex but not with insulin resistance in obese patients. *Arch. Physiol. Biochem*, 2010. 116(2): p. 57-62.

[133] D'Ambrosio, D.N., R.D. Clugston, and W.S. Blaner, Vitamin A Metabolism: An Update. *Nutrients*, 2011. 3(1): p. 63-103.

[134] Oda, N., et al., The ratio of leptin to adiponectin can be used as an index of insulin resistance. *Metabolism*, 2008. 57(2): p. 268-73.

[135] Plutzky, J., The PPAR-RXR transcriptional complex in the vasculature: energy in the balance. *Circ. Res*, 2011. 108(8): p. 1002-16.

In: Beta-Carotene

Editor: Maxime Lefevre

ISBN: 978-1-62417-173-4

© 2013 Nova Science Publishers, Inc.

Chapter 2

β-CAROTENE AND PEROXISOME PROLIFERATOR-ACTIVATED RECEPTOR GAMMA

Wen-en Zhao, Han Zhao, Han Zhang and Yong Li

School of Chemical Engineering and Energy,
Zhengzhou University, China

ABSTRACT

Peroxisome proliferator-activated receptor gamma (PPARγ), a member of the nuclear hormone receptor superfamily, functions as a transcription factor that regulates several biological processes, including growth and differentiation. It has been reported that PPARγ is involved in numerous physiological and pathological processes which β-carotene takes part in, such as antiproliferative action of β-carotene against cancer cells, and the inhibitory effects of β-carotene and its metabolites (vitamin A and its derivatives retinaldehyde and retinoic acid) on differentiation of pre-adipocytes into adipocytes and adiogenesis for the control of body adiposity. β-Carotene-15,15'-monooxygenase (Bcmo1) is the key enzyme for vitamin A production. *Bcmo1*, a PPARγ target gene, is inducedly expressed during adipocyte differentiation and highly expressed in mature adipocytes. Mice deficient in BCMO1 develop dyslipidemia and are susceptible to high fat diet-induced obesity. Dietary β-carotene decreased *PPARr* expression in adipose issue of vitamin A-deficient mice. In addition, PPARγ is also involved in some biological functions of other carotenoids, such as inhibitory effects of lycopene on the proliferation of prostate cancer cells, the anti-obesity effects of astaxanthin, bixin, β-cryptoxanthin, fucoxanthin and its metabolites, lycopene, and neoxanthin, modification of inflammatory responses by lutein and lycopene in macrophages stimulated, and the regulatory effects of lycopene on cholesterol synthesis and efflux in macrophages.

Keywords: β-Carotene, PPARγ, antiproliferative action, anti-obesity effects, modification of inflammation

INTRODUCTION

Peroxisome proliferator-activated receptor gamma (PPARγ), a member of the nuclear hormone receptor superfamily, functions as a ligand-activated transcription factor. It has been implicated in numerous physiological and pathological processes, such as adipocyte differentiation, insulin sensitivity, the growth of cells in various organs, and the occurrence of several human diseases including obesity, dyslipidemia, diabetes, inflammation, hypertension, atherosclerosis, and cancer [1-3]. Endogenous PPARγ ligands include 15-deoxy-Δ-^{12,14}- prostaglandin J_2 (15dPG-J_2) as well as linoleic, linolenic, and arachidonic acids. Pharmarceutical PPARγ ligands include the thiazolidinediones (ciglitazone, piglitazone, rosiglitazone, and troglitazone),which are some of the most commonly prescribed medications for the treatment of type II diabetes mellitus. The activated PPARγ formes a heterodimer with retinoic X receptor α (RXRα), and binds to its specific response elements termed peroxisome proliferating responsive elements (PPREs) in the promoter region of various target genes. PPARγ is expressed in a large number of human tissues such as breast, colon, lung, ovary, prostate, stomach, bladder, and thyroid, where it is demonstrated to regulate cell proliferation, differentiation, and apoptosis. This property makes PPARγ an important target for the development of new and effective anticancer therapies [4,5]. In recent years, it has been reported that PPARγ is involved in numerous biological processes which β-carotene and other carotenoids participate in, such as growth and apoptosis of cancer cells, adipocyte differentiation and adiogenesis, inflammatory responses, and cholesterol synthesis and efflux in macrophages, and so on.

1. PPARγ ACTIVATION IN β-CAROTENE-INHIBITED CANCER CELL PROLIFERATION

A wealth of epidemiological studies have reported that higher β-carotene plasma levels or dietary intake of β-carotene-rich foods are associated with a decreased risk of cancer [6-10]. Although intervention studies from the Alpha-Tocopherol, Beta-carotene Cancer Prevention Trial (ATBC) in Finland and the β-Carotene and Retinol Efficancy Trial(CARET) in USA have unexpectedly reported increased cancer rates in smokers and asbestos workers after high, long-term, β-carotene supplementation [11-13], there is evidence of beneficial effects of β-carotene supplementation against cancer in normal, healthy, nonsmoking populations [910]. The animal models and the cultured cells have been used to investigate the mechanisms of β-carotene-inhibited cancer proliferation. β-Carotene and other carotenoids have been observed to act as potent growth-inhibitory agents in several tumor cells, including breast, colon, prostate, lung, melanoma, and leukemia cells [14,15]. There are several mechanisms concerning the ability of β-carotene and other carotenoids to modulate the expression of proteins and transcription systems involved in cancer cell growth and apoptosis [16-19] .

The effects of β-carotene and other carotenoids on PPARγ-mediated pathways have also been studied in cancer cells. Sharoni and colleagues proposed in their reviews that some carotenoids, such as β-carotene, lycopene, phytoene, and phytofluene, caused the transactivation of peroxisome proliferator-response element (PPRE) in MCF-7 cells co-transfected with PPARγ. This activity was lower than that achieved with the known PPAR ligands, such as 15-deoxy-$\Delta^{12,14}$- prostaglandin J_2 and ciglitazone [19] . Takahashi et al reported that the treatment of such isoprenols as farnesol and geranylgeraniol caused the transactivation of PPARγ reporter gene and increased expression of PPAR-targeted lipid metabolic genes. However, they showed that various carotenoids at 100 μM, a concentration hardly achievable in aqueous solutions, did not significantly affect PPARγ transactivation [20] . These studies do not yet mention whether activation of the PPARγ system contributes to the inhibition of cancer cell growth by β-carotene and other carotenoids.

Interestingly, Hosokawa et al reported that combined treatment of 3.8 μM fucoxanthin, a carotenoid from the edible seaweed *Undaria pinnatifida*, with 10 μM troglitazone remarkably induced DNA fragmentation which led to the reduction on viability of human Caco-2 colon cancer cells. But 3.8 μM fucoxanthin and 10 μM troglitazone did not have significant effects on Caco-2 cell viability when used respectively. The authors did not investigate PPARγ acitivation [21]. Recently our experimental results showed that β-carotene remarkably inhibited cell proliferation and induced apoptosis, and enhanced the expression of PPARγ in breast cancer MCF-7 cells. GW9662, an irreversible antagonist of PPARγ, partly attenuated the cell death caused by β-carotene. In addition, β-carotene increased p21 and decreased cox-2 expression, and induced reactive oxygen species (ROS) production and cytochrome C release. The results suggest that the synergistic effect of PPARγ expression and ROS production may account for β-carotene-mediated anticancer activities [22]. Our another results demonstrated that β-carotene, astaxanthin, capsanthin, and bixin inhibited the proliferation and induced apoptosis of leukemia K562 cells in dose- and time-dependent manners, and interfered with cell cycle progression. Pretreatment with GW9662 partly attenuated the inhibition of K562 cell proliferation by the four carotenoids, respectively. These carotenoids up-regulated the expression of PPARγ, p21, and Nrf2, and down-regulated the expression of cyclin D1 in a dose-dependent manner. We suggest that PPARγ signaling pathway is involved in the inhibition of tumor cell proliferation by carotenoids including β-carotene [23]. Afterwards, Yang et al reported that lycopene treatment significantly inhibited the proliferation of androgen-dependent human prostate LNCaP cancer cells, increased the protein and mRNA expression of PPARγ and Liver X receptor alpha (LXRα) at 24 and 48 h, and decreased cellular total cholesterol levels and increased the expression of ATP-binding cassette transporter 1 (ABCA1) and apoA1 protein at 96 h. Incubation of LNCaP cells with lycopene in the presence of GW9662 and LXRα antagonist GGPP restored the cell proliferation to the control levels and significantly suppressed protein expression of PPARγ and LXRα as well as increased cellular total cholesterol levels. LXRα knockdown by siRNA against LXRα significantly enhanced the proliferation of LNCaP cells, whereas si-LXRα knockdown followed by incubation with lycopene restored the proliferation to the control level. They proposed that the anti- proliferative effect of lycopene on LNCaP cells involves the activation of the PPARγ-LXRα-A BCA1 pathway, leading to reduced cellular total cholesterol levels [24]. Their study in androgen - independent prostate cancer DU145 cells showed similar results. Furthermore, lycopene in combination with the LXRα agonist T0901317 exhibited synergistic effects on cell proliferation and protein expression of PPARγ,

LXRα, and ABCA1. Their results demonstrated that lycopene can inhibit DU145 cell proliferation via PPARγ-LXRα-ABCA1 pathway [25]. It appears to us that the up-regulation of PPARγ expression at least partly contributes to the antiproliferative effects of β-carotene and other carotenoids on cancer cells.

2. REPRESSION OF PPARγ EXPRESSION IN THE INHIBITORY EFFECTS OF β-CAROTENE AND OTHER CAROTENOIDS ON ADIPOCYTE DIFFERENTIATION AND ADIPOGENESIS

2.1. β-Carotene and Its Metabolite Retinoids (Vitamin A and Its Derivatives)

Obesity caused by excess accumulation of adipose tissue has become a medical problem in countries worldwide because it may increase the risk of various diseases, such as heart disease, type II diabetes, obstructive sleep apnea, and so on. Adipocyte differentiation is a complex process, in which a variety of transcription factors are involved. PPARγ is considered the master regulator of adipogenesis and in its absence adipocyte differentiation cannot proceed [26, 27].

The role of β-carotene in adipocyte biology has received more and more attention. Evidence from cell culture and animal model studies indicates that most actions of β-carotene in adipocyte differentiation and adipogenesis are mediated by its metabolites. β-Carotene is the natural precursor for apocarotenoid molecules including retinoids (vitamin A and its derivatives, such as retinaldehyde (Rald) and retinoic acid (RA)) [28]. It is oxidatively converted to retinaldehyde by β-carotene -15,15'- monooxygenase 1 (BCMO1) present in various tissues, including the intestine, liver, testes, and adipose tissue via central cleavage of β-carotene 1 [29,30]. Retinaldehyde can be oxidized to retinoic acid and also be reduced to retinol [31]. β-Carotene can also undergo asymmetric cleavage to yield apocarotenals and β-ionone by β-carotene -9',10'- dioxygenase 2 (BCDO2) [32,33]. The *BCMO1* gene has been shown to be transcriptionally regulated by the action of PPARs and RXRs in both mice and humans [34,35]. Kawada et al [36] reported that β-carotene, β-apo-8-carotenal, and retinal markedly inhibited the differentiation of 3T3-L1 preadipocyte to adipocytes. They suggested that the inhibitory action of adipocyte differentiation by carotenoids and retinoids was exhibited through the retinoic acid receptor (RAR) up-regulation and the suppression of PPARγ2. However, it is reported that β-carotene treatment at a concentration of 20 μM, but not 10 μM, in 3T3-L1 adipocytes during differentiation for 4 d enhanced the expression of genes related to insulin sensitivity, including PPARγ2, adipocyte lipid-binding protein, glucose transporter-4, and adiponectin protein in the medium [37]. A 9-*cis* *β*-carotene–enriched diet inhibited atherogenesis and fatty liver formation in LDL receptor knockout mice [38]. von Lintig group reported that on a diet providing β-carotene as major vitamin A precursor, vitamin A levels fell dramatically and the β-carotene accumulated in large quantities in several tissues examined in *BCMO1* knock-out mice. Mice deficient in BCMO1 developed dyslipidemia, such as fatty liver and elevated serum free fatty acids, and were more susceptible to high fat diet-induced obesity compared to wild mice. Bcmo1 knockout mice showed increased expression of PPARγ regulated genes in fat depots. BCMO1 was identified as the key enzyme for vitamin A production [39]. They also reported that *BCMO1* expression was induced during NIH 3T3-L1 adipocyte differentiation. β-Carotene but not all-*trans*-retinol decreased lipid content of mature adipocytes and was metabolized to retinoic acid (RA) in mature adipocytes. RA decreased the expression of PPARγ and CCAAT/ enhancer- binding protein α, key lipogenic transcription factors, and reduced the lipid content of mature adipocytes. Dietary β-carotene decreased *PPARr* expression in white adipose issue of vitamin A-deficient mice. However, *BCMO1*, which is a PPARγ target gene, is highly expressed in mature adipocytes, allowing for β-carotene to be converted to retinoic acid[40]. Recently, von Lintig group reported that BCMO1 knockout mice showed increased expression of BCDO2 in adipocytes and β-10′-apocarotenol accumulated as the major β-carotene derivative. In wild- type mice, dietary β-carotene significantly reduced body adiposity (by 28%), leptinemia and adipocyte size, resulted in a general down-regulation of gene expression in adipose tissue, and down-regulated PPARγ and PPARγ target genes. These effects of β-carotene were absent in BCMO1 knockout mice despite β-10′-apocarotenoid production, demonstrating that these effects were dependent on the BCMO1- mediated production of retinoids. The study showed that β-carotene plays an important role in the control of body fat reserves in mice and BCMO1 is a critical molecular player for the regulation of PPARγ activity in adipocytes [41].

In recent years, the importance of vitamin A and its derivatives, retinaldehyde (Rald) and retinoic acid (RA) from β-carotene, in adipose tissue biology and the development of adiposity has become apparent.

It has long been established that retinoic acid (RA) is an inhibitor of preadipocyte differentiation in cell culture [42, 43]. RA inhibited adipogenesis early in adipocyte differentiation by repressing the CCAAT/ enhancer binding protein β (C/EBPβ)-mediated transcription and decreasing PPARγ expression through binding to and activating retinoic acid receptors [44-47]. RA can no longer prevent adipocyte differentiation if added to the cell culture after early differentiation is completed [40,48]. Retinoic acid inhibited pig preadipocyte differentiation, activating RAR and downregulating PPARγ, retinoic acid X receptor (RXR)α, and sterol regulatory element binding protein1C [46,49]. Recently Berry et al reported that in mature adipocytes RA activated both RARs and PPAR β/δ, thereby enhancing lipolysis and depleting lipid stores. RA treatment of obese mice induced expression of PPAR β/δ and RAR target genes involved in regulation of lipid homeostasis, leading to weight loss and improved insulin responsiveness. The results indicated that suppression of obesity and insulin resistance by RA was largely mediated by PPAR β/δ and further enhanced by activation of RARs [50]. Berry et al also showed that RA inhibited adipocyte differentiation by activating the cellular RA binding protein type II (CRABP-II)/RARγ path in preadipose cells, thereby up-regulating the expression of the adipogenesis inhibitors Pref-1, Sox9, and Kruppel-like factor 2 (KLF2), and therefore pointed out that RA suppresses adipogenesis in vivo [51]. Dave et al reported that stem bromelain (SBM) inhibited adipogenesis irreversibly. SBM and all-trans retinoic-acid (atRA) treatment together inhibited adipocyte differentiation more effectively than either alone. SBM, together with atRA, may be a potent modulator of obesity by repressing the PPARγ-regulated adipogenesis pathway at all stages and by augmenting TNFα- induced lipolysis and apoptosis in mature adipocytes [52].

In contrast to above conclusions, García-Rojas et al indicated that 9-cis RA and atRA are powerful agents for the promotion of bovine adipogenesis. 9-cis RA and atRA increased PPARγ and PPARγ coactivator 1 (PGC-1α) mRNA expression in bovine adipogenic cultures, with 9-cis being a better activator. Expression of PPARγ mRNA was increased by 30 μM β-carotene, however, 10 μM β-carotene decreased the expression compared with differentiation medium. But it is not conclusive that activation of the PPAR system contributes to the ability of carotenoids to promote adipose tissue differentiation [53]. Krskova-Tybitanclova et al showed in an *in vivo* trial that

PPARγ mRNA was significantly increased in rat adipose tissue by 13-cis RA treatment [54]. Villarroya et al held that the final effect of RA on preadipocyte differentiation depends on the concentration and isomer availability, as well as on the relative RAR and RXR availability in the cells [55].

Ziouzenkova et al showed that Rald was present in rodent fat, can inhibit PPARγ-induced adipogenesis, and increased energy dissipation. In vivo, mice lacking the Rald-catabolizing enzyme retinaldehyde dehydrogenase 1 (Raldh1) resisted diet-induced obesity and insulin resistance. In vitro, Rald inhibited RXR and PPARγ activation. They identified Rald as a distinct transcriptional regulator of the metabolic responses to a high-fat diet [56,57]. They also found that β-apo-14'-carotenal (apo14), an asymmetric β-carotene cleavage product, can also inhibit PPARγ and PPARα responses. During adipocyte differentiation, apo14 inhibited PPARγ target gene expression and adipogenesis [58].

Retinol is very hydrophobic and is normally sequestrated by the retinol binding proteins [59]. Serum retinol binding protein 4 (RBP4), secreted by adipocytes, has been associated with insulin resistance [60]. Intracellularly, cellular retinol-binding proteins (CRBP) protect retinol from the cellular milieu and facilitate channeling of retinol toward specific enzymes required either for its oxidation to retinoic acid or for its esterification to retinyl esters [61-64]. Currently, three known CRBPs, termed CRBP-I, CRBP-II, and CRBP-III have been identified in murine tissues [63,65,66]. Vogel group reported that CRBP-I was a cytosolic protein specifically expressed in preadipocytes in adipose tissue that regulated adipocyte differentiation in part by affecting PPARγ activity. CRBP-I deficiency led to significantly enhanced adipocyte differentiation and increased intracellular TG accumulation due to augmented PPARγ activity [67]. They also showed that CRBP-III was present in adipocytes and a direct target of PPARγ activation. It was expressed during mid- and late-stage differentiation of adipocytes. The lack of CRBP-III was associated with decreased adipose tissue development and markedly down-regulated PPARγ activity. The function of CRBP-III is to facilitate the esterification of retinol to retinyl ester in the mammary gland during lactation [26,68,69]. It is well established that CRBP-II is expressed primarily in the small intestine and binds both retinol and retinaldehyde in the enterocyte. CRBP-II mediates intracellular retinoid transport and metabolism [70]. The effect of vitamin A deficiency on obesity might increase the risk of fat deposition and also the risk of chronic inflammation associated with obesity [71].

Although a growing body of evidence indicates that retinoic acid represses adipogenesis and reduces body fat reserves in tissues including brown and white adipose tissues, skeletal muscle and the liver, controversial data have been reported, particularly regarding retinoid effects on hepatic lipid and blood lipid profile [72,73]. This shows that the molecular mechanisms underlying retinoid effects on adipocyte differentiantion and adipogenesis are complex and remain incompletely understood. It is proposed that there is a high turnover of adipocytes at all adult ages in humans. Adiposity can be affected by retinoids throughout life, and particularly through long-lasting effects at critical developmental stages [74,75].

2.2. Other Carotenoids

In addition to β-carotene, other carotenoids also display the anti-obesity effects via PPARγ regulation. Astaxanthin improved the adipogenic differentiation potential of mouse neural progenitor cells(NSCs).

Astaxanthin-treated NSCs showed prominent fat formation and induced significant overexpression of adipogenesis-related AP and PPARγ mRNA [76]. Bixin and norbixin (annatto extracts) activated PPARγ and induced mRNA expression of PPARγ target genes such as aP2, lipoprotein lipase (LPL), and adiponectin in differentiated 3T3-L1 adipocytes and enhanced insulin-dependent glucose uptake [77].

Tsuchida et al reported that the oral intake of β-cryptoxanthin exerted anti-obesity effects by lowering visceral fat levels [78]. β-Cryptoxanthin inhibited lipid accumulation in 3T3-L1 cells, affected the cell differentiation through its function as a ligand of RARα and RARγ, and down-regulated mRNA expression of PPARγ.

Their results indicated that β-cryptoxanthin inhibited 3T3-L1 adipogenesis via the down-regulation of PPARγ through RAR activation [79]. Fucoxanthin is a major carotenoid present in edible seaweed such as *Undaria pinnatifida* and *Hijikia fusiformis*. Fucoxanthin and its metabolites, fucoxanthinol and amarouciaxanthin A, inhibitd the adipocyte differentiation of 3T3-L1 cells through down-regulation of PPARγ and C/EBPα [80-82]. Interestingly, Kang et al reported that fucoxanthin from the edible brown seaweed *Petalonia binghamiae* promoted 3T3-L1 adipocyte differentiation, increased triglyceride accumulation, increased protein expression of PPARγ, C/EBPα, sterol regulatory element-binding protein 1c (SREBP1c), adipocyte fatty acid-binding protein (aP2), and adiponectin mRNA expression during the early stage of differentiation (D0-D2). However, it reduced the expression of PPARγ, C/EBPα, and SREBP1c during the intermediate (D2-D4) and late stages (D4-D7) of differentiation.

Their results suggest that fucoxanthin exerts differing effects on 3T3-L1 cells of different differentiation stages [83]. Lycopene has been shown to be beneficial in protecting against high-fat diet-induced fatty liver. Dietary lycopene down-regulated BCMO1, PPARγ, and fatty acid binding protein 3 (FABP3) mRNA expression in rat kidney and adrenal. These data suggest that lycopene may play an important role in the modulation of β-carotene, retinoid, and/or lipid metabolism [84]. Apo-10'-lycopenoic acid(ALA), a lycopene metabolite converted by carotene 9',10'-oxygenase, protected against the development of steatosis in *ob/ob* mice by upregulating SIRT1 gene expression and activity [85]. Okada et al tested the suppressive effects of 13 naturally occurring carotenoids (lutein, violaxanthin, α-carotene, β-carotene 5,6-epoxide, canthaxanthin, citranaxanthin, rhodoxanthin, β-cryptoxanthin, antheraxanthin, lutein epoxide, capsorubin) on 3T3-L1 adipocyte differentiation.

They demonstrated that neoxanthin treatment significantly reduced intercellular lipid accumulation and glycerol-3-phosphate dehydrogenase activity and decreased the expression of C/EBPα and PPARγ mRNAs without affecting the expression of C/EBPβ and C/EBPγ mRNAs. The other 12 carotenoids used did not show the suppressive effects on adipose cell differentiation. Combined with their results on fucoxanthin and fucoxanthinol they suggested that carotenoids containing an allene bond and an additional hydroxyl substituent on the side group may show suppressive effects on adipocyte differentiation in 3T3-L1 cells [80-82,86]. It should be noted that their observation is not in agreement with the results obtained by Tsuchida et al using β-cryptoxanthin [79] and obtained by García-Rojas et al using lutein in a bovine adipocyte differentiation system, in which 30 μM lutein increased PPARγ mRNA expression [53]. Perhaps hydroxyl group at 3 position of ionone ring is also important for the carotenoid effects. It appears that carotenoids have a complex influence on PPARγ-regulated pathways controlling adipocyte differentiation and adipogenesis. In addition to structures of carotenoids, different differentiation stages and different organ resources of adipocyte may contribute to changeable effects.

3. PPARγ IN INFLAMMATORY RESPONSE MODIFICATION AND CHOLESTEROL SYNTHESIS AND EFFLUX REGULATION BY CAROTENOIDS

Immune cell macrophages induced by lipopolysaccharide (LPS) produce nitric oxide using inducible nitric oxide synthase (iNOS). iNOS is an important enzyme that mediates inflammatory processes. Improper up-regulation of iNOS is associated with pathophysiology of certain types of human cancers as well as inflammatory disorders including atherosclerosis [87]. It is well known that PPAR and retinoic acid X receptor (RXR) regulate immune function, including repression of NF-κB signaling and inflammatory cytokine production[88]. Selvaraj et al reported that dietary lutein and fat interacted to modify nitrite production in lipopolysaccharide (LPS)-stimulated macrophages. High levels of lutein increased nitrite production, however, high levels of fat reversed the stimulatory effect of lutein [89]. They also reported that there were significant interactive effects of lutein and dietary fat or eicosapentaenoic acid (EPA) on iNOS mRNA in LPS- stimulated chickens and HD11 cell lines. Increasing lutein with high fat (6%) or EPA (15 mmol/L EPA) increased PPARγ and RXRα mRNA levels. Lutein increased PPARα mRNA levels in both macrophages and HD11 cells and RXRγ mRNA levels in macrophages. GW9662, and LG101208, a RXR antagonist, prevented the lutein-induced iNOS mRNA regulation, respectively. They concluded that lutein and dietary fat or EPA interact to modulate iNOS mRNA levels through the PPARγ/RXR pathway in chickens and HD11 cell lines. Moreover, It also showed that lutein may play a role in the LPS-induced inflammatory responses through activating PPAR and RXR [90]. They investigated the effect of dietary lutein or polyunsaturated fatty acid (PUFA) fat on lutein and lipid content, PPAR and RXR expression in chicken immune tissues during inflammation to assess the modification of *in vivo* inflammatory responses by dietary PUFA fat and lutein [91]. Lutein in immune tissues was depleted during inflammation and the depletion extent was dependent on dietary lutein levels [92]. Similarly fat levels were modified during inflammation [93]. Selvaraj et al showed that LPS injection decreased the lutein content and increased the fat content in chicken liver and spleen. Dietary PUFA fat at 6% ameliorated the lutein depletion effect of LPS. Dietary lutein and PUFA fat content modulated liver and spleen PPAR (γ and α) and RXR (γ and α) isomers during the pro-inflammatory response to LPS. During LPS-stimulation, high dietary lutein or high PUFA fat increased the expression of all PPAR and RXR isomer mRNA levels. They pointed out that dietary lutein and PUFA fat were anti-inflammatory due to modification of immune tissue lutein content, PPAR, RXR isomers and IL-1β mRNA levels in liver and spleen, namely due to modification of immune responses to LPS stimulation [91]. To investigate the role of lycopene on smoke-driven inflammation in human THP-1 macrophages showed that lycopene inhibited cigarette smoke extract (CSE)-induced IL-8 production and NF-kB activation, decreased CSE-induced ROS production, and inhibited CSE-induced phosphorylation of the redox-sensitive ERK1/2, JNK and p38 MAPKs. Moreover, lycopene increased PPARγ levels which, in turn, enhanced PTEN expression and decreased pAKT levels in CSE-exposed cells. Such effects were abolished by the PPARγ inhibitor GW9662. Similar effects were also observed in isolated rat alveolar macrophages exposed to CSE. The results indicate that lycopene prevented CSE-induced IL-8 production through a mechanism involving an inactivation of NF-kB, accompanied by an inhibition of redox signalling and an activation of PPARγ signaling [94].

It is now well known that oxidized low-density lipoprotein (oxLDL) and oxysterols play important roles in atherogenesis [95,96]. Pro-inflammatory and/or pro-oxidative reactions induced by some oxysterols are major events involved in vascular dysfunction and atherogenesis. Oxysterols have been also reported to enhance pro-inflammatory cytokines secretion and expression [97]. Increased serum concentrations of oxysterols were recently associated with an increased risk of coronary atherosclerosis in humans [98]. Palozza et al reported that lycopene prevented oxysterol (7-keto-cholesterol and 25-hydroxycholesterol) -induced increase in the secretion and expression of pro-inflammatory cytokines, such as TNFα, IL-1β, IL-6 and IL-8 and increased PPARγ levels in human THP-1 macrophages. Lycopene was also able to inhibit oxysterol-induced ROS production as well as to suppress both redox-based MAPK phosphorylation and NF-κB activation. They suggest that lycopene exerted such a prevention through a mechanism involving an inhibition of NADPH oxidase, redox-sensitive MAPK expression, and NF-κB activation. Meantime lycopene could also reduce cytokine levels through an induction of PPARγ which further inhibited NF-κB activation [99]. Moreover, lycopene has been demonstrated to be able to prevent 7-ketocholesterol (7-KC)-induced oxidative stress and apoptosis in human THP-1 macrophages [100].

Hypercholesterolemia is also one of the most important risk factors for atherosclerosis. The deregulation of cholesterol homeostasis promotes foam cell formation in atherosclerosis [101]. Palozza et al also reported that macrophage enrichment with lycopene resulted in the suppression of cellular cholesterol synthesis and efflux. Lycopene may reduce intracellular levels of cholesterol in human THP-1 macrophages. This effect was accompanied by a decrease in the expression of 3-hydroxy-3-methylglutaryl coenzyme A (HMG-CoA) reductase, the rate-limiting enzyme in cholesterol synthesis, and by an enhancement of the expressions of ABCA1 and caveolin-1 (cav-1). Meantime lycopene modified the localization of RhoA GTPase in human macrophages, activating PARPγ and liver X receptor alpha (LXRα) expressions [101], which has been shown to play important roles in ABCA1 and cav-1-mediated cholesterol efflux [103,104]. They proposed a new cascade mechanism of lycopene in attenuating foam cell formation and preventing atherosclerosis which involved inhibition of HMG-CoA reductase, RhoA inactivation and subsequent increase in PPARγ and LXRα activities and enhancement of ABCA1 and cav-1 expressions [102]. It has been reported that β-carotene regulates HMG-CoA reductase expression by some post-transcriptional mechanisms [105].

The results described above show that lycopene plays its role of atherosclerosis preventionon through preventing oxysterol-induced pro-inflammatory responses and controlling cholesterol synthesis and efflux in human macrophages and the cascade mechanisms of these actions involve PPARγ activation. Lycopene is a potential anti- atherosclerotic nutrient.

CONCLUSION

As the roles of β-carotene and other carotenoids including lycopene in relation to health and disease have been progressively understood, elucidation about their molecular mechanisms of action has received more and more attention. In addition to their antioxidant activity, one of ways of their beneficial effects exerted by β-carotene and other carotenoids is transcriptional modulation of the important gene expression concerned. As an important transcription factor, PPARγ has been proved to be involved in anti-proliferation, anti-obesity, inflammation modification, and cholesterol homeostasis modulation of carotenoids, as reviewed in this paper. Furthermore, in recent years new research has emerged pointing to new molecular pathways, including PPARγ functioning, by which β-carotene and other carotenoids as well as their products and metabolites exert their effects. Ongoing studies will offer new insights into their biological activities and molecular mechanisms, and thereby will contribute to improved dietary or supplementation-based strategies and future therapeutic interventions using PPARγ as a potential target.

REFERENCES

[1]   Lehrke M, Lazar M A, The many faces of PPARgamma. *Cell,* 2005, 123: 993-999.

[2]   Feige J N, Gelman L, Michalik L, Desvergne B, Wahli W, From molecular action to physiological outputs: peroxisome proliferator-activated receptors are nuclear receptors at the crossroads of key cellular functions. *Prog. Lipid Res.*, 2006, 45: 120-159.

[3]   Semple R K, Chatterjee V K, O'Rahilly S, PPAR gamma and human metabolic disease. *J. Clin. Invest.*, 2006, 116: 581-589.

[4]   Han S, Roman J, Peroxisome proliferators-activated receptor γ: a novel target for cancer therapeutics? *Anticancer Drugs*, 2007, 18: 237-244.

[5]   Ondrey F, Peroxisome proliferator-activated receptor gamma pathway targeting in carcinogenesis: implications for chemoprevention. *Clin. Cancer Res.*, 2009, 15: 2-8.

[6]   van Poppel G, Goldbohm R A, Epidemiologic evidence for beta-carotene and cancer prevention. *Am. J. Clin. Nutr.*, 1995, 62: 1393s-1440s

[7]   Mayne S T, Beta-carotene, carotenoids, and disease prevention in humans. *FASEB J.*, 1996, 10: 690-701.

[8]   Kim J, Kim M K , Lee J K, Kim J H, Son S K, Song E S, Lee K B, Lee J P, Lee J M, Yun Y M, Intakes of vitamin A, C, and E, and beta-carotene are associated with risk of cervical cancer: a case-control study in Korea. *Nutr. Cancer-Intern. J.*, 2010, 62: 181-189.

[9]   Goralczyk, R, beta-Carotene and lung cancer in smokers: review of hypotheses and status of research. *Nutr. Cancer-Intern. J.*, 2009, 61: 767-774.

[10]   Touvier M, Kesse E, Clavel-Chapelon F, Boutron-Ruault M C, Dual association of beta-carotene with risk of tobacco-related cancers in a cohort of French women. *J. Natl. Cancer Inst.*, 2005, 97: 1338-1344.

[11]   The Alpha-Tocopherol, Beta Carotene Cancer Prevention Study Group, The effect of vitamin E and beta carotene on the incidence of lung

cancer and other cancers in male smokers. *N. Engl. J. Med.*, 1994, 330: 1029-1035.

[12] Omenn G S, Goodman G E, Thornquist M D, Balmes J, Cullen M R, Glass A, Keogh J P, Meyskens F L Jr, Valanis B, Williams J H Jr, Barnhart S, Cherniack M G, Brodkin C A, Hammar S, Risk factors for lung cancer and for intervention effects in CARET, the Beta-Carotene and Retinol Efficancy Trial. *J. Natl. Cancer Inst.*, 1996, 88: 1550-1559.

[13] Omenn G S, Goodman G E, Thornquist M D, , Effects of a combination of beta-carotene and vitamin A on lung cancer and cardiovascular disease. *N. Eng. J. Med.*, 1996, 334: 1150-1155.

[14] Gallicchio L, Boyd K, Matanoski G, Tao X, Chen L, Lam T K , Shiels M, Hammond E, Robinson K A, Laura E Caulfield, James G Herman, Eliseo Guallar, Alberg A J, Carotenoids and the risk of developing lung cancer: a systematic review. *Am. J. Clin. Nutr.*, 2008, 88: 372-383.

[15] Nishino H, Murakoshi M, Tokuda H, Satomi Y, Cancer prevention by carotenoids. *Arch. Biochem. Biophys*, 2009, 483: 165-168.

[16] Palozza P, Serini S, Nicuolo F D, et al, β-Carotene exacerbates DNA oxidative damage and modifiers p53-related pathways of cell proliferation and apoptosis in cultured cells exposed to tobacco smoke condensate. *Carcinogenesis*, 2004, 25: 1315-1325.

[17] Palozza P, Serini S, Torsello A, et al, Mechanism of activation caspase cascade during β-carotene-induced apoptosis in human tumor cells. *Nutr. Cancer*, 2003, 47: 76-87.

[18] Palozza P, Can β-carotene regulate cell growth by a redox mechanism? An answer from cultured cells. *Biochim. Biophys. Acta.*, 2005, 1740: 215-221.

[19] Sharoni Y, Danilenko M, Dubi N, Ben-Dor A, Levy J, Carotenoids and transcription. *Arch. Biochem. Biophys.*, 2004, 430: 89–96.

[20] Takahashi N, Kawada T, Goto T, et al, Dual action of isoprenols from herbal medicines on both PPARγ and PPARα in 3T3-L1 adipocytes and HepG2 hepatocytes. *FEBS Lett.*, 2002, 514: 315–322.

[21] Hosokawa M, Kudo M, Maeda H, et al, Fucoxanthin induces apoptosis and enhances the antiproliferative effect of the PPARgamma ligand, troglitazone, on colon cancer cells. *Biochim. Biophys. Acta.*, 2004, 1675: 113-119.

[22] Cui Y, Lu Z, Bai L, Shi Z, Zhao W, Zhao B, β-Carotene induces apoptosis and up-regulates peroxisome proliferators-activated γ

expression and reactive oxygen species production in MCF-7 cancer cells. *Eur. J. Cancer*, 2007, 43: 2590-2601.

[23] Zhang X, Zhao W, Hu L, Zhao L, Huang J, Carotenoids inhibit proliferation and regulate expression of peroxisome proliferators-activated receptor gamma (PPARγ) in K562 cancer cells. *Arch. Biochem. Biophys.*, 2011, 512: 96-106.

[24] Yang C M, Lu I H, Chen H Y, Hu M L, Lycopene inhibits the proliferation of androgen-dependent human prostate tumor cells through activation of PPARγ-LXRα-ABCA1 pathway. *J. Nutr. Biochem.*, 2012, 23: 8-17.

[25] Yang C M, Lu I H, Chen H Y, Hu M L, Lycopene and the LXRα agonist T0901317 synergistically inhibit the proliferation of androgen-independent prostate cancer cells via the PPARγ-LXRα-ABCA1 pathway. *J. Nutr. Biochem.*, 2011, Nov 30.

[26] Frey S K, Vogel S, Vitamin A metabolism and adipose tissue biology. *Nutrients*, 2011, 3: 27-39.

[27] Rosen E D, MacDougald O A, Adipocyte differentiation from the inside out. *Nat. Rev. Mol. Cell Biol.*, 2006, 7: 885–896.

[28] von Lintig J, Colors with functions: elucidating the biochemical and molecular basis of carotenoid metabolism. *Annu. Rev. Nutr.*, 2010, 30: 35–56.

[29] Paik J, During A, Harrison E H, Mendelsohn C L, Lai K, Blaner W S, Expression and characterization of a murine enzyme able to cleave β-carotene: the formation of retinoids. *J. Biol. Chem.*, 2001, 276: 32160–32168.

[30] Redmond T M, Gentleman S, Duncan T, Yu S, Wiggert B, Gantt E, Cunningham F X Jr, Identification, expression, and substrate specificity of a mammalian β-carotene 15,15′- dioxygenase. *J. Biol. Chem.*, 2001, 276: 6560–6565.

[31] Duester G, Mic F A, Molotkov A, Cytosolic retinoid dehydrogenases govern ubiquitous metabolism of retinol to retinaldehyde followed by tissue-specific metabolism to retinoic acid. *Chem. Biol. Interact.*, 2003, 143–144: 201–210.

[32] Kiefer C, Hessel S, Lampert J M, Vogt K, Lederer M O, Breithaupt D E, von Lintig J, Identification and characterization of a mammalian enzyme catalyzing the asymmetric oxidative cleavage of provitamin A. *J. Biol. Chem.*, 2001, 276: 14110–14116.

[33] Lobo G P, Amengual J, Palczewski G, Babino D, von Lintig J, Mammalian carotenoid- oxygenases: key players for carotenoid function and homeostasis. *Biochim. Biophys. Acta.*, 2012, 1821: 78–87.

[34] Boulanger A, McLemore P, Copeland N G, Gilbert D J, Jenkins N A, Yu S S, Gentleman S, Redmond T M, Identification of beta-carotene-15,15′-monooxygenase as a peroxisome proliferators-activated receptor target gene. *FASEB J.*, 2003, 17: 1304–1306.

[35] Gong X, Tsai S W, Yan B, Rubin L P, Cooperation between MEF2 and PPARgamma in human intestinal beta,beta-carotene 15,15′-monooxygenase gene expression. *BMC Mol. Biol.*, 2006, 7: 7.

[36] Kawada T, Kamei Y, Fujita A, et al, Carotenoids and retinoids as suppressors on adipocyte differentiation via nuclear receptors. *Biofactors,* 2000, 13:103-109.

[37] Kameji H, Mochizuki K, Miyoshi N, Goda T, β-Carotene accumulation in 3T3-L1 adipocytes inhibits the elevation of reactive oxygen species and the suppression of genes related to insulin sensitivity induced by tumor necrosis factor-alpha. *Nutrition*, 2010, 26: 1151-1156.

[38] Harari A, Harats D, Marko D, Cohen H, Barshack I, Kamari Y, Gonen A, Gerber Y, Ben-Amotz A, Shaish A, A 9-*cis* β-carotene–enriched diet inhibits atherogenesis and fatty liver formation in LDL receptor knockout mice. *J. Nutr.*, 2008, 138: 1923-1930.

[39] Hessel S, Eichinger A, Isken A, Amengual J, Hunzelmann S, Hoeller U, Elste V, Hunziker W, Goralczyk R, Oberhauser V, von Lintig J, Wyss A, CMO1 deficiency abolishes vitamin A production from beta-carotene and alters lipid metabolism in mice. *J. Biol. Chem.*, 2007, *282*: 33553–33561.

[40] Lobo G P, Amengua J, Li H N, Golczak M, Bonet M L, Palczewski K, von Lintig J, Beta,beta-carotene decreases peroxisome proliferator receptor gamma activity and reduces lipid storage capacity of adipocytes in a beta,beta-carotene oxygenase 1-dependent manner. *J. Biol. Chem.*, 2010, 285: 27891–27899.

[41] Amengual J, Gouranton E, van Helden Y G J, Hessel S, Kramer J R, Kiec-Wilk B, Razny U, Lietz G, Wyss A, Dembinska-Kiec A, Palou A, Keijer J, Landrier J F, Bonet M L, von Lintig J, Beta-Carotene reduces body adiposity of mice via BCMO1. *PLoS ONE*, 2011, 6(6): e20644.

[42] Kuri-Harcuch W, Differentiation of 3T3-F442A cells into adipocytes is inhibited by retinoic acid. *Differentiation*, 1982, 23: 164–169.

[43] Sato M, Hiragun A, Mitsui H, Preadipocytes possess cellular retinoid binding proteins and their differentiation is inhibited by retinoids. *Biochem. Biophys. Res. Commun.*, 1980, 95: 1839– 1845.

[44] Ribot J, Felipe F, Bonet M L, Palou A, Changes of adiposity in response to vitamin A status correlate with changes of PPAR gamma 2 expression. *Obes. Res.*, 2001, 9: 500–509.

[45] Moon H S, Guo D D, Song H H, Kim I Y, Jiang H L, Kim Y K, Chung C S, Choi Y J, Lee H G, Cho C S, Regulation of adipocyte differentiation by PEGylated all-trans retinoic acid: Reduced cytotoxicity and attenuated lipid accumulation. *J. Nutr. Biochem.*, 2007, 18: 322–331.

[46] Suryawan A, Hu C Y, Effect of retinoic acid on differentiation of cultured pig preadipocytes. *J. Anim. Sci.*, 1997, 75: 112–117.

[47] Schwarz E J, Reginato M J, Shao D, Krakow S L, Lazar M A, Retinoic acid blocks adipogenesis by inhibiting C/EBPbeta-mediated transcription. *Mol. Cell Biol.*, 1997, 17: 1552–1561.

[48] Xue J C, Schwarz E J, Chawla A, Lazar M A, Distinct stages in adipogenesis revealed by retinoid inhibition of differentiation after induction of PPARgamma. *Mol. Cell Biol.*, 1996, 16: 1567–1575.

[49] Brandebourg T D, Hu C Y, Regulation of differentiating pig preadipocytes by retinoic acid. *J. Anim. Sci.*, 2005, 83: 98–107.

[50] Berry D C, Noy N, All- *trans*-retinoic acid represses obesity and insulin resistance by activating both peroxisome proliferation-activated receptor beta/delta and retinoic acid receptor. *Mol. Cell Biol.*, 2009, 29: 3286-3296.

[51] Berry D C, DeSantis D, Soltanian H, Croniger C M, Noy N, Retinoic acid upregulates preadipocyte genes to block adipogenesis and suppress diet-induced obesity. *Diabetes*, 2012, 61: 1112-1121.

[52] Dave S, Kaur N J, Nanduri R, Dkhar H K, Kumar A, Gupta P, Inhibition of adipogenesis and induction of apoptosis and lipolysis by Stem Bromelain in 3T3-L1 adipocytes. *PLoS ONE*, 2012, 7(1): e30831.

[53] García-Rojas P, Antaramian A, Gonzalez-Davalos L, Villarroya F, Shimada A, Varela-Echavarría A, Mora O, Induction of peroxisomal proliferator-activated receptor γ and peroxisomal proliferator-activated receptor γ coactivator 1 by unsaturated fatty acids, retinoic acid, and carotenoids in preadipocytes obtained from bovine white adipose tissue. *J. Anim. Sci.*, 2010, 88: 1801-1808.

[54] Krskova-Tybitanclova K, Macejova D, Brtko J, Baculikova M, Krizanova O, Zorad S, Short term 13-cis-retinoic acid treatment at

therapeutic doses elevates expression of leptin, GLUT4, PPARgamma and aP2 in rat adipose tissue. *J. Physiol. Pharmacol.*, 2008, 59: 731–743.

[55] Villarroya, F, Giralt M, Iglesias R, Retinoids and adipose tissues: Metabolism, cell differentiation and gene expression. *Int. J. Obes.*, 1999, 23: 1–6.

[56] Ziouzenkova O, Orasanu G, Sharlach M, et al, Retinaldehyde represses adipogenesis and diet-induced obesity. *Nat. Med.*, 2007, 13: 695–702.

[57] Ziouzenkova O, Plutzky J, Retinoid metabolism and nuclear receptor responses: New insights into coordinated regulation of the PPAR-RXR complex. *FEBS Lett.*, 2008, 582: 32–38.

[58] Ziouzenkova O, Orasanu G, Sukhova G, et al, Asymmetric cleavage of beta-carotene yields a transcriptional repressor of retinoid X receptor and peroxisome proliferator-activated receptor responses. *Mol. Endocrinol.*, 2007, 21: 77-88.

[59] Szuts E Z, Harosi F I, Solubility of retinoids in water. *Arch. Biochem. Biophys.*, 1991, 287: 297-304.

[60] Yang Q, Graham T E, Mody N, Preitner F, Peroni O D, Zabolotny J M, Kotani K, Quadro L, Kahn B B, Serum retinol binding protein 4 contributes to insulin resistance in obesity and type 2 diabetes. *Nature*, 2005, 436: 356–362.

[61] Noy N, Retinoid-binding proteins: Mediators of retinoid action. *Biochem. J.*, 2000, 348: 481–495.

[62] Blaner W S, Piantedosi R, Sykes A, Vogel S, Retinoic acid synthesis and metabolism. In *Retinoids*: The Biochemical and Molecular Basis of Vitamin A and Retinoid Action, Nau H, and Blaner W S, eds, Springer-Verlag, Berlin, 1999, Vol. 139, pp. 117–149.

[63] Ong D E, Newcomer M E, Chytil F, Cellular retinoid-binding proteins. In The Retinoids, Biology, Chemistry, and Medicine, 2nd ed, Sporn M B, Roberts A B, Goodman D S, eds, Raven Press, New York, 1994, pp. 283–317.

[64] Napoli J L, A gene knockout corroborates the integral function of cellular retinol-binding protein in retinoid metabolism. *Nutr. Rev.*, 2000, 58: 230–236.

[65] Piantedosi R, Ghyselinck N, Blaner WS, Vogel S, Cellular retinol-binding protein type III is needed for incorporation into milk. *J. Biol. Chem.*, 2005, 280: 24286-24292.

[66] Vogel S, Mendelsohn C L, Mertz J, Piantedosi R, Waldburger C, Gottesman M E, Blaner W S, Characterization of a new member of the

fatty acid-binding protein family that binds all-trans-retinol. *J. Biol. Chem.*, 2001, 276: 1353–1360.

[67] Zizola C F, Frey S K, Jitngarmkusol S, Kadereit B, Yan N, Vogel S, Cellular retinol-binding protein type I (CRBP-I) regulates adipogenesis. *Mol. Cell Biol.*, 2010, 30: 3412–3420.

[68] Zizola C F, Schwartz G J, Vogel S, Cellular retinol-binding protein type III is a PPARγ target gene and plays a role in lipid metabolism. *Am. J. Physiol. Endocrinol. Metab.*, 2008, 295: E1358–E1368.

[69] Piantedosi R, Ghyselinck N, Blaner W S, Vogel S, Cellular retinol-binding protein type III is needed for retinoid incorporation into milk. *J. Biol. Chem.*, 2005, 280: 24286–24292.

[70] E X, Zhang L, Lu J, Tso P, Blaner W S, Levin M S, Li E, Increased neonatal mortality in mice lacking cellular retinol-binding protein II. *J. Biol. Chem.*, 2002, 277: 36617–36623.

[71] Garcia O P, Effect of vitamin A deficiency on the immune response in obesity. *Proceed Nutr. Soc.*, 2012, 71: 290-297.

[72] Safonova I, Darimont C, Amri E Z, Grimaldi P, Ailhaud G, Reichert U, Shroot B, Retinoids are positive effectors of adipose cell differentiation. *Mol. Cell Endocrinol.*, 1994, 104: 201–211.

[73] Bost F, Caron L, Marchetti I, Dani C, Le Marchand-Brustel Y, Binetruy B, Retinoic acid activation of the ERK pathway is required for embryonic stem cell commitment into the adipocyte lineage. *Biochem. J.*, 2002, 361: 621–627.

[74] Spalding K L, Arner E, Westermark P O, Bernard S, Buchholz B A, Bergmann O, Blomqvist L, Hoffstedt J, Naslund E, Britton T, Concha H, Hassan M, Ryden M, Frisen J, Arner P. Dynamics of fat cell turnover in humans. *Nature*, 2008, 453: 783–787.

[75] Bonet M L, Ribot J, Palou A, Lipid metabolism in mammalian tissues and its control by retinoic acid. *Biochim. Biophys. Acta.*, 2012, 1821: 177–189.

[76] Kim J H, Nam S W, Kim B W, Kim W J, Choi Y H, Astaxanthin improves the proliferative capacity as well as the osteogenic and adipogenic differentiation potential in neural stem cells. *Food Chem. Toxicol.*, 2010, 48: 1741–1745.

[77] Takahashi N, Goto T, Taimatsu A, Egawa K, Katoh S, Kusudo T, Sakamoto T, Ohyane C, Lee J Y, Kim Y I, Uemura T, Hirai S, Kawada T, Bixin regulates mRNA expression involved in adipogenesis and enhances insulin sensitivity in 3T3-L1 adipocytes through PPAR. *Biochem. Biophys. Res. Commun.*, 2009, 390: 1372–1376.

[78] Tsuchida T, Mukai K, Mizuno Y, Masuko K, MinagawaK, The comparative study of β-cryptoxanthin derived from Satsuma mandarin for fat of human body. *Jpn. Pharmacol. Ther.*, 2008, 36: 247-253.

[79] Shirakura Y, Takayanagi K, Mukai K, Tanabe H, Inoue M, β-Cryptoxanthin suppresses the adipogenesis of 3T3-L1 cells via RAR activation. *J. Nutr. Sci. Vitaminol.*, 2011, 57: 426-431.

[80] Maeda H, Hosokawa M, Sashima T, Funayama K, Miyashita K, Fucoxanthin from edible seaweed Undaria pinnatifida, shows antiobesity effect through UCP1expression in white adipose tissues. *Biochem. Biophys. Res. Commun.*, 2005, 332: 392-397.

[81] Maeda H, Hosokawa M, Sashima T, Takahashi N, Kawada T, Miyashita K, Fucoxanthin and its metabolite, Fucoxanthinol, suppress adipocyte differentiation in 3T3-L1 cells. *Int. J. Mol. Med.*, 2006, 18: 147-152.

[82] Yim M J, Hosokawa M, Mizushina Y, Yoshida H, Saito Y, Miyashita K, Suppressive effects of amarouciaxanthin A on 3T3-L1 adipocyte differentiation through down-regulation of PPARγ and C/EBPα mRNA expression. *J. Agric. Food Chem.*, 2011, 59: 1646-1652.

[83] Kang S l, Ko H C, Shin H S, Kim H M, Hong Y S, Lee N H, Kim S J, Fucoxanthin exerts differing effects on 3T3-L1 cells according to differentiation stage and inhibits glucose uptake in mature adipocytes. *Biochem. Biophys. Res. Commun.*, 2011, 409: 769-774.

[84] Zaripheh S, Nara T Y, Nakamura M T, and Erdman J W Jr, Dietary lycopene downregulates carotenoid 15,15'-monooxygenase and PPAR-γ in selected rat tissues. *J. Nutr.*, 2006, 136: 4 932-938.

[85] Chung J, Koo K, Lian F, Hu K Q, Ernst H, Wang X D, Apo-10'-lycopenoic acid, a lycopene metabolite, increases Sirtuin 1 mRNA and protein levels and decreases hepatic fat accumulation in ob/ob mice. *J. Nutr.*, 2012, 142: 405-410.

[86] Okada T, Nakai M, Maeda H, Hosokawa M, Sashima T, Miyashita K, Suppressive effect of neoxanthin on the differentiation of 3T3–L1 adipose cells. *J. Oleo. Sci.*, 2008, 57: 345–351.

[87] Surh Y J, Chun K S, Cha H H, Han S S, Keum Y S, Park K K, Lee S S, Molecular mechanisms underlying chemopreventive activities of anti-inflammatory phytochemicals: down-regulation of COX-2 and iNOS through suppression of NF-[kappa]B activation. *Mutat. Res.*, 2001, 480–481: 243–268.

[88] Debril M B, Renaud J P, Fajas L, Auwerx J, The pleiotropic functions of peroxisome proliferator- activated receptor gamma. *J. Mol. Med.*, 2001, 79: 30–47

[89] Selvaraj R K, Koutsos E A, Calvert C C, Klasing K C, Dietary lutein and fat interact to modify macrophage properties in chicks hatched from carotenoid depleted or repleted eggs. *J. Anim. Physiol. Anim. Nutr.*, 2005, 90: 70–80.

[90] Selvaraj R K, Klasing K C, Lutein and eicosapentaenoic acid interact to modify iNOS mRNA levels through the PPARγ/RXR pathway in chickens and HD11 cell lines. *J. Nutr.*, 2006, 136: 1610–1616.

[91] Selvaraj R K, Shanmugasundaram R, Klasing K C, Effects of dietary lutein and PUFA on PPAR and RXR isomer expression in chickens during an inflammatory response. *Comp. Biochem. Physiol.*, Part A 157 (2010) 198–203.

[92] Koutsos E A, Calvert C C, Klasing K C, The effect of an acute phase response on tissue carotenoid levels of growing chickens (Gallus gallus domesticus). *Comp Biochem Physiol A Mol. Integr. Physiol.*, 2003, 135: 635–646.

[93] Contreras-Shannon V, Ochoa O, Reyes-Reyna S M, Sun D, Michalek J E, Kuziel W A, McManus L M, Shireman P K, Fat accumulation with altered inflammation and regeneration in skeletal muscle of CCR2-/- mice following ischemic injury. *Am. J. Physiol. Cell Physiol.*, 2007, 292: C953–C967.

[94] Simone R E, Russo M, Catalano A, Monego G, Froehlich K, Boehm V, Palozza P, Lycopene inhibits NF-kB-mediated IL-8 expression and changes redox and PPARγ signalling in cigarette smoke–stimulated macrophages. *PLoS ONE*, 2011, 6(5): e19652.

[95] Colles S M, Maxson J M, Carlson S G, Chisolm G M, Oxidized LDL-induced injury and apoptosis in atherosclerosis. Potential roles for oxysterols. *Trend. Cardiovasc. Med.*, 2001, 11: 131–8.

[96] Brown A J, Jessup W, Oxysterols and atherosclerosis. *Atherosclerosis*, 1999, 142: 1–28.

[97] Hansson G K, Immune mechanisms in atherosclerosis. *Arterioscler Thromb. Vasc. Biol.*, 2001, 21: 1876–80.

[98] Yasunobu Y, Hayashi K, Shingu T, Yamagata T, Kajiyama G, Kambe M, Coronary atherosclerosis and oxidative stress as reflected by autoantibodies against oxidized low-density lipoprotein and oxysterols. *Atherosclerosis*, 2001, 155: 445–53.

[99] Palozza P, Simone R, Catalano A, Monego G, Barini A, Mele M C, Parrone N, Trombino S, Picci N,. Ranelletti F O, Lycopene prevention of oxysterol-induced proinflammatory cytokine cascade in human

macrophages: inhibition of NF-κB nuclear binding and increase in PPARγ expression. *J. Nutr. Biochem.*, 2011, 22: 259–268.

[100] Palozza P, Simone R, Catalano A, Boninsegna A, Böhm V, Fröhlich K, Mele M C, Monego G, Ranelletti F O, Lycopene prevents 7-ketocholesterol-induced oxidative stress, cell cycle arrest and apoptosis in human macrophages. *J. Nutr. Biochem.*, 2010, 21: 34–46.

[101] Goldstein J L, Brown M S, Cholesterol quartet. *Science*, 2001, 292: 1310–1312.

[102] Palozza P, Simone R, Catalano A, Parrone N, Monego G, Ranelletti F O, Lycopene regulation of cholesterol synthesis and efflux in human macrophages. *J. Nutr. Biochem.*, 2011, 22: 971–978.

[103] Oram J F, ATP-binding cassette transporter A1 and cholesterol trafficking. *Curr. Opin. Lipidol.*, 2002, 13: 373–81.

[104] Hu Q, Zhang X J, Liu C X, Wang X P, Zhang Y, PPARγ1-induced caveolin-1 enhances cholesterol efflux and attenuates atherosclerosis in apolipoprotein E-deficient mice. *J. Vasc. Res.*, 2010, 47: 69–79.

[105] [Morenoav F S, Rossiellob M R, Manjeshwarb S, Nathb R, Raob P M, Rajalakshmib S, Sarmab D S R, Effect of p-carotene on the expression of 3-hydroxy-3-methylglutaryl coenzyme A reductase in rat liver. *Cancer Lett.*, 1995, 96: 201-208.

In: Beta-Carotene   ISBN: 978-1-62417-173-4
Editor: Maxime Lefevre   © 2013 Nova Science Publishers, Inc.

Chapter 3

BETA-CAROTENE: FUNCTIONS, HEALTH BENEFITS, ADVERSE EFFECTS AND APPLICATIONS

L. M. J. Carvalho[1], Dellamora-G. Ortiz[1], E. M. G. Ribeiro[1], L. Smiderle[1], E. J. Pereira[1] and J. L. V. Carvalho[2]

[1]Federal University of Rio de Janeiro, Faculty of Pharmacy,
Rio de Janeiro, Brazil
[2]Embrapa Food Technology, Guaratiba, Rio de Janeiro, Brazil

ABSTRACT

The purpose of this chapter is to review the main functions, benefits and possible adverse effects of beta-carotene on human health and its applications in food. More than 600 carotenoids have been identified from vegetable and animal sources, which possess varying levels of pro-vitamin A activity. Carotenoids from vegetables provide approximately 68% of the vitamin A ingested in the diet. According to FAO (2003), approximately 500 million people suffer from the effects of vitamin A deficiency, such as xerophthalmia, and each year three million malnourished people go blind due to insufficient vitamin A. The antioxidant capacity of carotenoids, i.e., ability to prevent peroxidation, is most likely responsible for their ability to protect against the detrimental health effects of vitamin A deficiency. Subclinical vitamin A deficiency, in which visible signs of xerophthalmia are absent, intensifies the severity of certain illnesses, such as diarrhea and other infectious diseases, eventually resulting in immunodeficiency of exclusively nutritional origin. Other roles have also been described for carotenoids in humans, the best known of which is their capacity to be converted into retinols (provitamin A activity). In addition to their function as the macular pigment of the eye, these substances are involved in a series of cellular processes, including the modulation of the inflammatory response, protection against cancer, prevention of cardiovascular diseases and cataracts, and antioxidant activity. The main carotenoids involved in human health are beta-carotene, alpha-carotene, lycopene, lutein, beta-cryptoxanthin and zeaxanthin, which can be found in blood plasma. Except for zeaxanthin, these compounds are easily obtained from foods; beta-carotene is the most abundant in the human diet. However, the absorption and utilization of carotenoids are influenced by several factors, such as the type and physical form of dietary carotenoids, the ingestion of fat, vitamin E and fibers, and the presence of certain diseases and parasite infection. The provitamin A carotenoid *cis*-isomer *(Z)* is converted less readily into vitamin A than is the *trans*-isomer *(E)*. Recently, *(all-E)*-beta-carotene was reported to be absorbed preferentially over (9-*Z*)-beta-carotene in humans. Few adverse effects related to the ingestion of supraphysiological doses of beta-carotene have been described. In rats, excess beta-carotene consumption had a positive effect on the control of arterial hypertension that did not affect biological parameters and had no detectable toxic effects. Due to the controlled conversion of beta-carotene into vitamin A, overconsumption does not cause hypervitaminosis A. In fact, the excessive ingestion of beta-carotene usually leads to carotenodermia, a reversible condition that results in an orange color in the skin due to beta-carotene deposition in the outermost layer of the epidermis. Carotenodermia is often observed in patients with hyperlipidemia, diabetes mellitus or hyperthyroidism. Moreover, it was reported that the combination of beta carotene and vitamin A may have had an adverse effect on the incidence of lung cancer and the risk of death from lung cancer, cardiovascular disease, or any other cause in smokers and workers exposed to asbestos.

INTRODUCTION

1. General Aspects

Carotenoids are natural pigments that are present in fruits and vegetables (Di Mascio et al., 2001) and can also be found in algae, fungi, bacteria and animals. More than 600 carotenoids have been isolated from vegetable and animal sources, with varying levels of pro-vitamin A activity (Palace et al., 1999). These substances have been suggested to play a protective role against diseases such as cancer and atherosclerosis (Di Mascio et al., 2001).

Carotenoids can only be biosynthesized by plants and microorganisms. Their presence in animals and accumulation in certain tissues like flamingo feathers, egg yolks and invertebrate exoskeletons is attributed to ingestion via food. In plants, carotenoids are located in subcellular organelles, namely chloroplasts and chromoplasts. In the chloroplasts, they are associated with specific proteins and act as photoprotective pigments and membrane stabilizers during photosynthesis (Schieber, 2005).

Carotenoids from vegetables provide approximately 68% of the vitamin A ingested in the diet. According to FAO (2003), approximately 500 million people suffer from the effects of insufficient vitamin A, such as xerophthalmia, and each year three million malnourished people go blind due to vitamin A deficiency.

2. CAROTENOIDS AND BETA-CAROTENE

These substances can be divided into two classes: carotenoids containing only carbon and hydrogen atoms, and the oxicarotenoids (xanthophylls), containing at least one oxygen atom. Based on the number of double bonds, multiple cis / trans configurations are possible for the same molecule, these isomerizations may occur due to chemical reactions, light radiation and thermal energy (Tapiero et al., 2003).

Structurally, vitamin A (retinol) is essentially half of a β-carotene molecule linked to a water molecule at the end of a polyene chain (Rodrigues-Amaya (2001) (Figure 1).

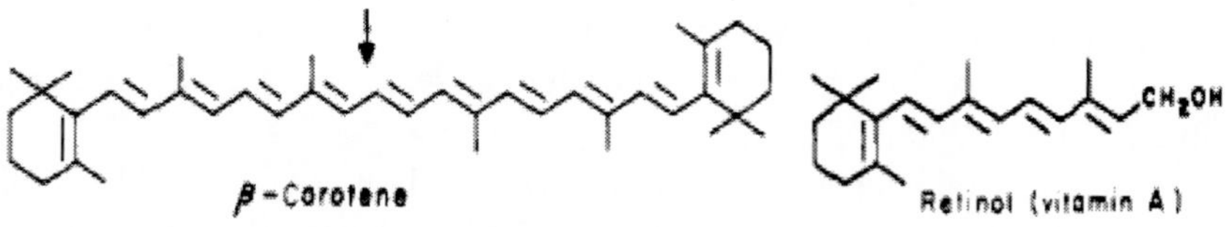

Figure 1. β-carotene and Vitamin A (Retinol).

Compared to vitamin A, carotenoids are more stable with respect to light and oxidation, possibly due to its location in the plant tissues. However, exposure to oxygen and heat treatments may result in destruction of the provitamin A carotenoids (Gayathri et al., 2004).

Seo et al. (2005) found lutein, lycopene, cryptoxanthin, α-carotene, β-carotene and *cis* β-carotene isomers in raw pumpkins (*Cucurbita moschata*). Among these compounds, β-carotene was the most abundant, followed by α-carotene.

High concentrations of O_2 can reduce the antioxidant activity of β-carotene, and studies conducted in pulmonary tissues and peripheral tissues revealed that the carotenoid effectiveness may be greater in peripheral tissues because the oxygen pressure is lower (Cerqueira, Medeiros & Augusto, 2007).

β-carotene is able to capture free radicals at the oxygen pressures commonly found in most tissues under physiological conditions. Each molecule of β-carotene can react with a number of free radical molecules, leading to the formation of stable products for periods up to one hour, even after exposure to air, under *in vitro* conditions (Cardoso, 1997).

Among the carotenoids, β-carotene exhibits the highest pro-vitamin A activity (100%) in biological tests with rats (Zemplei, Bowman & Russell, 2001).

Carotenoids with vitamin A activity, such as β-carotene, are considered pro-vitaminic until they are enzymatically cleaved at the central C15 - C15 ' oxidative bond in the intestinal mucosa to release two active molecules of retinol. The natural configuration of most carotenoid types in plants is the *trans* isomer. Because these are highly unsaturated compounds, they are susceptible to isomerization and oxidation during food processing and storage. The isomerization of the *trans-cis*-carotenoids into cis carotenoids is promoted by exposure to acidity, heat and light, which decreases both the color and vitamin A activity of the food (Ambrósio, Fields & Faro, 2006).

The occurrence of vitamin A deficiency in the northeastern regions of Brazil, where cassava is grown and is part of the normal diet, puts this culture in a privileged position with a viable alternative to combat hidden hunger (Ortiz & Nassar, 2006).

In animals and humans, carotenoids, particularly β-carotene and lycopene, protect against photo-oxidation by peroxyl radicals and can interact synergistically with other antioxidants. The vitamins in this group are important metabolic carotenoids. The structure of vitamin A (retinol) is derived from the di-terpene oxidative metabolism of tetraterpenoids, especially β-carotene obtained in the diet, which occurs in mammals. The cleavage or rupture of β-carotene occurs in the intestinal mucosal cells and is catalyzed by the O_2-dependent dioxygenase enzyme, most likely via a peroxide intermediate. Over 600 carotenoids are known, but only 20 are found in plasma and tissues. Lycopene is the most abundant carotenoid in human plasma and has a half-life of 2-3 days, according Tapiero et al. (2004), but lycopene shows no pro-vitamin A activity (Setiawan, et al., 2001; Micronutrient, 2002).

Table 1 shows the effects of β-carotene dose in studies of cancer carried out *in vivo*.

3. DIETARY RECOMMENDATIONS

It is estimated that carotenoids from vegetables contribute to approximately 68% of the dietary vitamin A worldwide and 82% in developed countries. One benefit of pro vitamin substances is that they are only converted to vitamin A when the body needs more of this vitamin, thus preventing its overaccumulation. Several factors influence the absorption and utilization of provitamins, such as the type and physical form of the carotenoids in the diet, fat intake, vitamin E, fiber and the presence of certain diseases and parasitic infections (Souza & Boas, 2002).

Campos et al. (2003) studied the amount of carotenoids in vegetables and concluded that 100 g of raw carrot can provide an average of 627 g RAE (Retinol Activity Equivalent), representing approximately 70% of the daily recommendation of vitamin A for an adult male between 19 and 50 years of age (900 μg RAE). Comparatively, fortified milk has 240 μg of RAE/100 g; thus, it would be necessary to consume 375 mL of fortified milk to reach the recommended intake of vitamin A. Considering that milk is an inaccessible resource for the poorest of the population due to its market value and lack of distribution in areas with little access to industrial products, plant sources are the most affordable way to meet the nutritional deficiencies of these populations.

RAE (Retinol Activity Equivalent). 1 RAE = 1 μg retinol; 12 μg β-carotene, 24 μg α-carotene or 24 μg β-cryptoxanthin. The dietary RAE for provitamin A carotenoids is two times larger than the retinol equivalent (RE). However, the RAE of preformed vitamin A is the same as the RE.

4. BETA-CAROTENE EXTRACTION, QUANTIFICATION AND IDENTIFICATION

The analysis of carotenoids involves extraction, saponification (when necessary), and mobile phase chromatography. The methodology currently used for carotenoid analysis is high performance liquid chromatography (HPLC), although these findings are often confirmed by open column chromatography and mass spectrometry (Rodriguez-Amaya, Kimura & Amaya-Farfan, 2008).

In the extraction, several water miscible solvents (for fresh products) and immiscible solvents (for dry products) are used, typically acetone and petroleum ether. Different solvents are used for the mobile phase; however, complete separations have been observed with a combination of methanol and methyl tert-butyl ether. The C30 column is typically used because of its high selectivity and resolution. Difficulties related to the cost and quality of analytical standards have contributed to the use of extracts isolated from natural sources as standards by many researchers (Mercadante, 1999; Sander et al., 2000; Nunes & Mercadante, 2006).

Bushway (1986) demonstrated that high performance liquid chromatography (HPLC-HPLC) analysis is a fast, simple and reproducible method for the identification of carotenoids, and some isomers may also be separated from fruits and vegetables.

According to Cortes et al. (2004), several methods have been described for determination of carotenoids. HPLC has been chosen as the best method of separation, identification and quantification of carotenoids found in biological tissues.

According to Lessin et al. (1997), the analysis of carotenoids in fresh and processed samples by reverse phase HPLC enabled the observation of chemical changes in some thermally processed vegetable and fruits, namely the transformation of the cross-β-carotene to the cis-geometrical isomer, β-carotene.

Lessin et al. (1997) found that a reverse phase C30 column could be used for the separation of cis and trans isomers of β-carotene under isocratic analysis conditions, but in some extracts (carrot, orange juice and tomato), it was necessary to separate carotenoids like xanthophylls that coelute with α-carotene and β-carotene prior to the analysis.

Table 1. The effects of β-carotene *in vivo* at different sites and steps of experimental carcinogenesis

Site	Animal	Carci-nogen	β-carotene dose	Effect	References
Skin	Rat (without skin)	UV-B radiation	1 g/kg of the diet	reduced cancer incidence (when administered afterUV-B)	Mathews-Roth & Krinsky (1987)
	Rat (Sencar)	DMBA + TPA	0.6 g/kg of the diet (after DMBA)	inhibited the conversion of papilloma to carcinoma	Chen et al. (1993)
	Rat	DMBA + TPA	2 × 200 nmol / weeks (topical application, with TPA)	reduced tumor incidence	Nishino (1995)
Oral cavity (lining of the bag facial)	Hamster (Syrian)	DMBA + BP	DMBA + 3 × 190 ng/mL BP /weeks (topical application)	reduced tumor incidence (when applied with or after DMBA)	Suda et al. (1986)
	Hamster	DMBA	2 × 250 mg/week (topical application after DMBA)	inhibited the appearance of tumors in 100% of animals	Gijare et al. (1990)
Liver	rat (Wistar)	DEN + 2-AAF (RH model)	70 mg/kg body weight body (airway gastric days alternate	inhibited the incidence of precancerous lesions (if given before DEN or continuously)	Moreno et al. (1991 e 1995a)
	rat (Sprague - Dawley)	2 – AAF (0.05% in the diet	0.1 g/kg of the diet	inhibited the incidence of precancerous lesions (if provided before the AAF or continuously)	Sarkar et al. (1994)
	rat (Wistar, SPF)	DEN + 2-AAF+ PHB	0.3 g / kg diet i.p. - 9 × 1 mg/kg body weight	no effect (administered before and after DEN)	Astorg et al. (1996)
Colon	Rat (F-344)	AOM	0, 1, 10 or 20 mg/kg diet (↑fat ↓ or ↑ in fiber)	inhibited the incidence of pre-neoplastic and neoplastic (administered continuously)	Alabaster et al. (1995)
Pancreas	rat (Wistar)	AZA	0.1 and 1 g/kg or + Se (1 or 2 mg/kg diet)	inhibited the incidence of precancerous lesions (when administered concomitant with and after AZA)	Appel & Woutersen (1996)

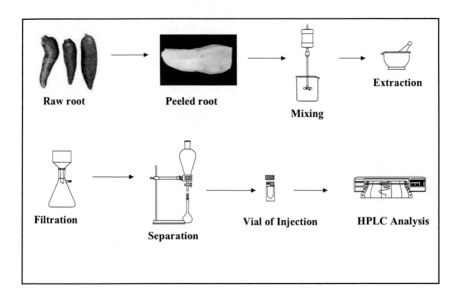

Figure 2. Scheme of carotenoid extraction from cassava for HPLC analysis (Oliveira, 2006).

According to Britton (1995), the carrot (*Daucus carota* L.) is one of the best sources of α-carotene and β-carotene. Nevertheless, purity of the standards must be at least 90% (Rodriguez-Amaya & Kimura, 2004). Figure 2 shows the beta-carotene standard extraction. Oliveira (2006) found that β-carotene prepared from carrots (Figures 3 and 4) was 93.99% pure.

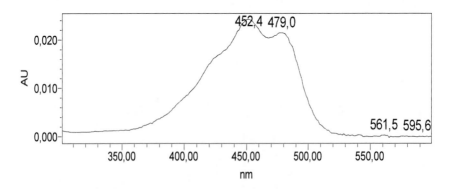

Figure 3. β-carotene UV Absorption Spectrum. Source: Oliveira (2007).

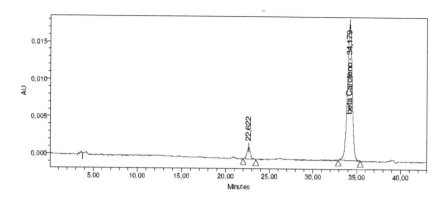

Figure 4. HPLC chromatogram of the β-carotene standard.

Several factors can affect the qualitative and quantitative composition of carotenoids in foods, such as variety/cultivar, season, the tissue (plant part) sampled, growth conditions, and post-harvest handling, processing and storage conditions. Because carotenoids are highly unstable and oxidizable, several factors may cause the loss of its biological activity or total loss of the molecule (Penteado, 2003, Rodriguez-Amaya, Kimura & Amaya-Farfan, 2008).

5. BENEFITS TO HUMAN HEALTH

The main carotenoids involved in human health are beta-carotene, alpha-carotene, lycopene, lutein, beta-cryptoxanthin and zeaxanthin, which can be found in blood plasma. Except for zeaxanthin, these compounds are easily obtained from food, and beta-carotene is the most abundant in the diet (Silva & Mercadante, 2002; Penteado, 2003; Rodriguez-Amaya & Kimura, 2004).

Fifty carotenoids have provitamin A activity, and the most important precursor is β-carotene (Olson, 1987). The other important precursors are α-carotene and β-cryptoxanthin, which each has at least one ionone ring at the end of the isoprenoid structure (Meléndez-Martínez, Vicario & Heredia, 2004).

In addition to their roles as vitamin A precursors, other health benefits have been suggested for carotenoids, such as the prevention of certain cancers, protection of gastric mucosa against ulcers, capacity to prevent photosensitization in certain skin diseases, increase of immune response to infection and anti-aging properties (Bako, Delhi & Tóth, 2002). Carotenoids can also be converted into retinols (provitamin A activity). Furthermore, in addition to their role as the macular pigments of the eye, these substances have antioxidant activity and are involved in a series of cellular processes, such as modulating inflammatory response, protecting against cancer, preventing cardiovascular diseases and cataract.

The antioxidant capacity of carotenoids is most likely responsible for their ability to protect against the detrimental health effects of vitamin A deficiency. Subclinical vitamin A deficiency, in which visible signs of xerophthalmia are absent, intensifies the severity of certain illnesses, such as diarrhea and other infectious diseases, eventually resulting in immunodeficiency of exclusively nutritional origin (Ramalho et al., 2008).

6. ADVERSE EFFECTS ON HUMAN HEALTH

Few adverse effects related to the ingestion of supraphysiological doses of beta-carotene have been described. In rats, the consumption of excess beta-carotene has a positive effect on the control of arterial hypertension that did not affect biological parameters and had no detectable toxic effects (Oliveira et al., 2007).

However, due to the controlled conversion of beta-carotene into vitamin A, overconsumption does not cause hypervitaminosis A. The excessive ingestion of beta-carotene usually leads to carotenodermia, a reversible condition which produces an orange color in the skin, resulting from beta-carotene deposition in the outermost layer of the epidermis. Carotenodermia is often observed in patients with hyperlipidemia, diabetes mellitus and hyperthyroidism. However, high doses of beta-carotene have been associated with an increased incidence of lung cancer in smokers (News Medical, 2012).

7. BIOAVAILABILITY OF CAROTENOIDS AND THEIR APPLICATIONS

The absorption and utilization of carotenoids are influenced by several factors, such as the type and physical form of dietary carotenoids, the ingestion of fat, vitamin E and fibers, and by certain diseases and parasite infections (Souza & Boas, 2002).

It is estimated that carotenoids from vegetables and fruits provide more than 70% of vitamin A in the human diet in more than thirty countries of the world. Carotenoid bioavailability and metabolism are affected by many factors, including the properties of the food matrix, food preparation, coingestion with fat and fiber, gastrointestinal diseases and malnutrition status. They can also influence the translation or transduction of certain genes and may act as inhibitors of regulatory enzymes. In this context, they have been discussed as active in cancer prevention (Stahl & Sies, 2005).

The interest in plant materials that contain provitamin A carotenoid activity has increased significantly in recent years, considering that these micronutrients can help counteract the nutritional deficiencies observed in low-income populations and the populations of developing countries (Ambrósio, Fields & Faro, 2006).

The provitamin A carotenoid cis-isomer (Z) is less readily converted into vitamin A than is the trans-isomer (E). Recently, (all-E)-beta-carotene was reported to be absorbed preferentially over (9-Z)-beta-carotene in humans (Stahl et al., 1995; Ben-Amotz, Levy, 1996; Stahl & Sies, 2003).

Ortega-Flores et al. (2003) evaluated the bioavailability of beta-carotene in cassava leaves using a model of hepatic depletion of vitamin A reserved in rats. The results showed that the bioavailability of β-carotene in the cassava leaves was lower compared to synthetic β-carotene. Similar results were found in studies conducted by Bulux *et al.* (1996) and Tanumihardjo (2002).

Carotenoid absorption and transport are similar to those of lipids. After ingestion, carotenoids are incorporated into mixed micelles composed of bile acids, fatty acids, monoglycerides and phospholipids. Absorption occurs without cleavage, but carotenoids such as β-carotene and cryptoxanthin are partially converted to retinal by hydrolysis within the intestinal cells. Subsequently, the retinal is converted to retinol and transported in the lymph vessels to the liver by chylomicrons in the form of esters of retinol. The retinol is then stored in the liver, which stores 90% of the vitamin A into the body (Ambrósio, Campos & Faro, 2006).

In vivo structural alterations of the all-trans, 9-cis and 13-cis β-carotene isomers were studied in a biological assay to verify the possible structural interconversion of the 9-cis, 13-cis and all-trans-beta-carotene isomers. Different pure β-carotene isomers (either all-trans-β-carotene, all 9-cis or all 13-cis-β-carotene) were administered for 15 days to rats that had been previously depleted of liver carotenoids. The *in vivo* re-isomerization of the isomers was verified. The 9-cis isomer can be converted into all-trans-β-carotene, all-trans-β-carotene re-isomerized into 9-cis, and 13-cis was re-isomerized into 9-cis and all-trans-β-carotene. The authors concluded that the 13-cis-β-carotene was more susceptible to isomerization than the 9-cis because

9-cis could be isomerized into all-trans but not into 13-cis, while the 13-cis could be modified to either 9-cis or all-trans-β-carotene (Costa, Ortega-Flores & Penteado, 2002).

Thakkar et al. (2007) studied the β-carotene accessibility in 10 cassava cultivars (processed by boiling for 30 minutes) with varying concentrations of β-carotene using a coupled *in vitro* digestion/Caco-2 cell uptake model. All-trans, 9-cis, and 13-cis β-carotene were the most abundant carotenoids in raw cassava, and recoveries after digestion exceeded 70%. The efficiency of micellization of total β-carotene was 30% for various cultivars, with no significant difference in isomers and linearly proportional to the concentration in cooked cassava. The accumulation of all-trans β-carotene by Caco-2 cells incubated with the diluted micelle fraction for 4 h was proportional to the quantity present in micelles. These results suggest that all-trans β-carotene content appears to provide the key selection marker for breeding cassava to improve Vitamin A status and that a more complicated screening procedure using *in vitro* digestion coupled to cell uptake does not provide additional information about potential bioavailability.

8. BETA-CAROTENE IN RAW MATERIALS AND IN PROCESSED AND HOME COOKED FOOD

β-carotene is the most abundant of the various carotenoids existing in vegetables, especially in yellow leaves and fruits and vegetables such as papaya, pear, kale, spinach and pumpkin. The maintenance of the natural carotenoid color after processing and during storage is the major concern of the food industry (Dutta et al., 2005; Clydesdale et al. 1970; Ihl et al., 1998).

Beta-carotene, among other carotenoids, has been shown to have an important and positive effect on human health. This compound is commonly found in many vegetables, and cooking can modify its activity. Twenty-five fresh vegetables were submitted to three common Chinese domestic cooking methods - boiling, stir-frying and deep-frying. Boiling preserved the majority of carotenoids, whereas stir-frying and deep-frying did not. Cilantro (fresh) showed the highest total and *trans*-β-carotene contents (3.19 and 1.92 μmol × 10^2 g fresh vegetable, respectively) followed by fern, sweet potato leaves, vegetable fern and Thai basil leaf. An overall increase of 9-Z isomers was observed in all boiled vegetables, most likely because of E/Z isomerization, which could result in the formation of more bioactive compounds, such as (9-

Z)-β-carotene. Boiling may be the preferred domestic cooking method to preserve carotenoids in vegetables (Chiu *et al.*, 2012).

Wada et al. (2005) determined the most common carotenoids and trans- and cis-isomers in raw vegetables and the impact of bioactive compounds after Chinese cooking practices (boiling, stir-frying, and deep-frying). The cilantro, Thai basil leaf, sweet potato leaf, and choy sum exhibited the highest total carotenoid contents (TCC). Boiling preserved the majority of the carotenoids, whereas stir-frying and deep-frying significantly decreased TCC and (all-E)- forms of carotenoids.

These results show that it is important to consider the effects of home cooking, industrial processing and storage methods to reduce micronutrient loss.

Normally, the real retention percentage (% RR) is calculated according to Murphy, Criner, Gray (1975) by the formula:

%RR= $\dfrac{\text{carotenoids content per gram of cooked sample x weight (g) cooked sample}}{\text{carotenoids content per gram of raw sample x weight (g) of raw sample}} \times 100$

Depending on the time and temperature applied, different levels of degradation and isomerization of carotenoids occur. Blanching, pasteurization and sterilization processes cause *trans-cis* isomerization, while more aggressive thermal processing destroys the carotenoids (Pérez-Gálvez et al., 2005).

Gayathri *et al.* (2004) found that the β-carotene loss in carrots (27%) was greater when cooked under pressure for 10 min than when cooked in boiling water (16%).

A similar study was conducted by Pinheiro - Sant'ana et al. (1998) in carrots using different cooking processes (steam cooking, cooking in water with and without pressure, moist/dry cooking and conventional dehydration). The total carotenoid retention ranged from 60.13 to 85.64%. Water cooking promoted a higher retention of α-carotene (63% to 70) and β-carotene (65% to 77%) than other methods. Despite the significant carotenoid losses, carrots prepared at home remain a rich source of provitamin A under different processing conditions. Blanching for three and five minutes in boiling water increased the β-carotene content compared with fresh carrots, possibly due to the higher extractability caused by boiling or to moisture and soluble solids losses that concentrate the sample (Dutta et al, 2005).

However, it should be noted that thermal processing promotes the isomerization of carotenoids in food from *trans (E)* to *cis* (Z) and that the degree of isomerization is directly related to the intensity and duration of heat treatment (Rock et al., 1998). Rodrigues & Penteado (1989) concluded that, nutritionally, the differentiation between the *cis* and *trans* isomers of provitamins is important because the *cis* form (Z) has lower activity.

Figure 5 shows the colors of yellow sweet cassava roots before (raw) and after cooking.

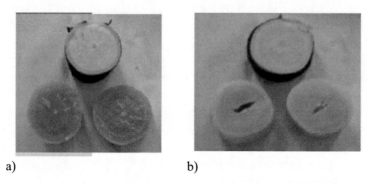

a)   b)

Figure 5. Yellow Sweet Cassava Root Samples: a) red color and intense color after cooking in water; b) yellow color and intense yellow color after cooking in water (Oliveira, 2006).

Melo et al. (2009) concluded that vegetables subjected to steaming exhibited differential antioxidant properties, with broccoli and pumpkin (squash) displaying antioxidant activity greater than 70%. The highest DPPH radical sequestration activities were observed in cauliflower, carrots and spinach and did not differ from the action of the synthetic antioxidant BHT. Therefore, the application of heat did not drastically affect the antioxidant properties of vegetables in these systems and models.

Oliveira (2006) evaluated yellow bitter cassava roots before and after flour processing and storage for 26 days. The total carotenoid losses after 19 days of storage ranged from 86 to 99%, and the average degradation found in all the roots just after processing (time zero) was 50%. The exposure of the carotenoids to heat during the flour process was the main degradation factor (oxidation) (Bauernfeind, 1972).

Losses of α and β-carotene and its 9 and 13-*cis*-β-carotene isomers were observed in pumpkins (*C. moschata*) after steaming or cooking in boiling water. The steamed pumpkins presented the highest α and β-carotene contents. The α-carotene contents were lower than the *trans* (E)-β-carotene contents in both pumpkin samples (raw and cooked). An increase in the 13-cis-β-carotene isomer was observed after both cooking methods (Neves, 2011).

Similarly, Oliveira (2006) found that *trans (E)*-β-carotene was the most abundant carotenoid in yellow sweet cassava after cooking.

Rodriguez-Amaya et al. (2011) evaluated the carotenoid compositions of sweet potato roots, cassava roots and corn kernels, observing that β-carotene predominates in sweet potato and cassava, while lutein and zeaxanthin prevail in corn. The major carotenoid of orange-fleshed sweet potatoes (OFSP) is all-*trans*-β-carotene, and the consumption of this vegetable has been shown to improve the vitamin A status of children. These authors suggested that OFSP flour can be used as a substitute for wheat flour in bakery products other than breads.

APPROACHES

As observed throughout this chapter, beta-carotene, although possessing high provitamin A and antioxidant activities, may lose these activities during the cooking process and even during preparation. Another important factor is its bioaccessbility, which should be studied further. The results of studies regarding the improvement of vegetable matrices may improve access to foods with high beta-carotene content, appropriate for addressing the nutritional needs of low-income populations.

REFERENCES

Alabaster, O.; Tang, Z. C.; Frost, A. & Shivapurkar, N. (1995). Effect of β-carotene and bran fiber on colonic aberrant crypt and tumor formation in rats exposed to azoxymethane and high dietary fat. Carcinogenesis, 16 (1), 127-132.

Ambrósio, C. L. B.; Campos, F. A. C. S. & Faro, Z. P. (2006). Carotenoides como alternativa contra a hipovitaminose A. Revista Nutrição, 19 (2), 233-243.

Appel, M. J. & Woutersen, R.A. (1996). Effects of dietary β-carotene and selenium on initiation and promotion of pancreatic carcinogenesis in azaserine-treated rats. Carcinogenesis, 17 (7), 1411-1416.

Astorg, P.; Gradelet, S.; Bergès, R. & Suschetet, M. (1996). No evidence for an inhibitory effect of β-carotene or of canthaxanthin on the initiation of liver preneoplastic foci by diethylnitrosamine in the rat. Nutrition and Cancer, 25 (1), 27-34.

Bakó, E.; Deli, J. & Tóth, G. (2002). HPLC study on the carotenoid composition of calendula products. Journal of Biochemical and Biophysical Methods, 53, 242-250.

Bauernfeind, J.C. (1972). Carotenoid vitamin A precursors and analogs in foods and feeds. J Agric Food Chem. May-Jun, 20 (3), 456-73.

Bushway, R.J.; Yang, A. & Yamani, A.M. (1986). Comparison of alpha- and beta carotene content of supermarket versus roadside stand produce. J. Food Qual., 9 (6), 437-443.

Ben-Amotz, A. & Levy, Y. (1996). Bioavailability of a natural mixture compared with synthetic all-trans b-carotene in human serum. American Journal of Clinical Nutrition, 63, 729-734.

Britton, G. (1995). Structure and properties of carotenoids in relation to function. The FASEB Journal, 9, 155 -158.

Bulux, J.; Serrano, J. Q. ; Perez, R. ; Rivera, C.; Lopez, C.Y. & Solomons, U. W. (1996). Studies on the bioconversion and bioavailability of β-caroteno in Guatemala school chidren. European Journal of Clinical Nutrition, 50 (3), 876-877.

Campos, M. F., Sant'Ana, H. M. P., Stringheta, P., C. & Chaves, J. B. P. (2003). Beta-carotene contents in vegetables prepared in Viçosa, Minas Gerais, Brazil restaurants. Braz. J. Food Technol, 6 (2), 163-169.

Cardoso, L. S. (1997). Carotenoids photophyisics and the antioxidant role of carotenoides e of the B-carotene. Química Nova, 20(5): 535-540.

Cerqueira, M. F.; Medeiros, M. H. G. & Augusto, O. (2007). Dietary antioxidants: controverse and perspectives. Química Nova, 30 (2), 441-449.

Chen, L-C.; Sly, L.; Jones, C.S.; Tarone, R. & De Luca, L.M. (1993). Differential effects of dietary β-carotene on papilloma and carcinoma formation induced by an initiation - promotion protocol in SENCAR mouse skin. Carcinogenesis, 14 (4), 713-717.

Clydesdale F. M.; Fleischman, D. L. & Francis, F. L. (1970). Maintenance of color in processed green vegetables. Journal of Food Prod. Dev., 4, 127-130.

Costa, M. A. L.; Ortega-Flores, C. I. & Penteado, M. V. C. (2002). Alterações estruturais in vivo dos isômeros 9 cis e 13 cis do β-caroteno. Ciência e Tecnologia de Alimentos, 22 (3), 224-228.

Cortes, C.; Esteve, M. J.; Frigola, A. & Terregrosa, F. (2004). Identification and quantification of carotenoids including geometrical isomers in fruit and vegetables juices by liquid chromatography with ultraviolet-diode array detection. Journal of Agricultural and Food Chemistry, 52, 2203-2212.

Di Mascio, P.; Matos, H. R.; Yamagughi, L. F.; Miyamoto, S.; Marques, S. A. & Medeiros, M. H. G. (2001). Carotenoides e Saúde: Mecanismo de Ação. Quarto Simpósio Latino Americano de Ciência de Alimentos. Departamento de Bioquímica, Instituto de Química, Universidade de São Paulo, Brasil.

Dutta, D.; Raychaudhuri, U. & Chahraborty, R. (2005). Retention of β-caroteno in frozen carrots under varying conditions of tempeture and time of storage. African Journal of Biotechnology, 4 (1), 103-106.

FAO - Food and Agriculture Organization of de United Nations. Statistical Database –FAOSTAT, (2003). Available from: <http://faostat.fao.org/>. Acessed in 30 april, 2012.

Gayathri, G. N.; Platel, K.; Prakash, J. & Srinivasan, K. (2004). Influence of antioxidant spices on the retention of β-carotene in vegetables during domestic cooking processes. Food Chemistry, 84, 35-43.

Gijare, P.S.; Rao, K.V.K. & Bhidg, S.V. (1990). Modulatory effects of snuff, retinoic acid, and β-carotene on DMBA - induced hamster cheek pouch carcinogenesis in relation to keratin expression. Nutrition and Cancer, 14 (3-4), 253-259.

Ihl, M.; Monslaves, M. & Bifani, V. (1998). Chlorophylase inactivation as a measure of blanching efficiency and color retention of artichokes (*Cynara scolyus* L.). Lebensmittel-Wissenschaft und-Technologie, 31, 50-56.

Lessin, W., J., Catigani, G., L., Schwartz, S., J. (1997) Quantification of cis-trans isomers of provitamin A carotenoids in fresh and processed fruits and vegetables. J Agric Food Chem., 45(10), 3728-32.

Mathews-Roth, M. M.; Krinsky, N. I. (1987). Carotenoids affect development of UV-B induced skin cancer. Photochemistry and Photobiology, 46(4), 507-509.

Meléndez-Martínez, A. J.; Vicario, I. M. & Heredia, F. J. (2004). Importancia nutricional de los pigmentos carotenoides. Archiv. LatinoAmeric Nutric., 54 (2), 149-155.

Melo, E. A, Maciel, M. I. S., Arroxelas, G. L. & Santana, A. P. M. (2009). Antioxidant capacity of vegetables submited to heat treatment. Rev. Soc. Bras. Nutr., São Paulo, SP, 34 (1), 85-95.

Mercadante, A. Z. (1999). Chromatographic separation of carotenoids. Archiv. LatinAmerican Nutric., 49, 52S-57S.

Nunes, I. L. & Mercadante, A. Z. (2006). Vantagens e desvantagens das colunas C_{18} e C_{30} para separação de carotenóides por CLAE. Rev Bras. Ciênc. Farmac., 42, 539-546.

Moreno, F. S.; Rizzi, M. B. S. L.; Dagli, M. L. Z. & Penteado, M. C. V. (1991). Inhibitory effects of β-carotene on preneoplastic lesions induced in wistar rats by the resistant hepatocyte model. Carcinogenesis, 12 (10), 1817-1822.

Murphy, E. W.; Criner, P. E. & Gray, B. C. (1975). Journal of Agricultural and Food Chemistry, 23, 1153.

Neves, A.C. (2011). Total carotenoids, β-carotene and trans (E) and cis (Z) isomers in pumpkin (Cucurbita moschata Duch) landraces raw and retention study of α e β –carotene after steam cooking and by immersion in water cooking methods. MsC Thesis in Pharmaceutical Sciences. Rio de Janeiro Federal Univesity, Rio de Janeiro, Brazil.

News Medical (2012). Beta-Carotene Side Effects. New Medical, Available from: < http://www.news-medical.net/health/Beta-Carotene-Side-Effects-(Portuguese).aspx. Acessed in 26 July, 2012.

Nishino, H. (1995). Cancer chemoprevention by natural carotenoids and their related compounds. Journal of Cellular Biochemistry, Supplement 22, 231S-235S.

Oliveira, A. R. G. (2006). Evaluation and retention study of total carotenoids and β-carotene in bitter and sweet yellow cassava. MsC Thesis in Food Science and Technology. Technology Institute. Rio de Janeiro Rural Federal Univesity, Seropédica, Rio de Janeiro, Brazil.

Oliveira, G. S.; Figueiredo, A. S. P.; Santos, R. S. & Vianna, L. M. (2007). Effect of beta-carotene supplementation on the blood pressure of rats. Revista de Nutrição, 20(1), 39-45.

Olson, J. A. (1987). Recommended dietary intakes (RDI) of vitamin A in humans. American Journal of Clinical Nutrition, 45, 704-716.

Ortega-Flores, C.I.; Lopes da Costa, M. A.; Cereda, M.P. & Camargo Penteado, M. V. (2003). Bioavailability of â-carotene of the dried cassava leaves (Manihot esculenta, Crantz). Ciência Tecnologia de Alimentos, 23 (3), 473-477.

Ortiz, R. & Nassar, N.M.A. (2006). Cassava improvement to enhance livelihoods in Sub-Saharan Africa and Northeastern Brazil. First

International Meeting on Cassava Breeding, Biotechnology and Ecology, Brasilia, Brazil, 11-15.

Palace, V.; Hill, M.H.; Farahmand, F. & Singal, P.K. (1999). Mobilization of antioxidant vitamin pools and hemodynamic function following myocardial infarction. Circulation, 99, 121-126.

Penteado, M.V.C. (2003). Vitaminas: aspectos nutricionais, bioquímicos, clínicos e analíticos. Barueri, São Paulo: Manole, 74p.

Pérez-Gálvez, A., Jarém-Galán, M. & Mínguez-Mosquera, M. I. (2005). Impact of the increased thermal processing on retinol equivalent values of paprika oleoresins. Journal of Food Engineering, 71 (4), 379-385.

Pinheiro-Sant'ana, H.M.; Stringueta P. C.; Brandão, S. C. C.; Páez H. H. & Queiróz, V. M. V. (1998). Evaluation of total carotenoids, α- and β-carotene in carrots (Daucus carota L.) during home processing. Ciência Tecnologia de Alimentos, 18 (1), 39-44.

Ramalho, A.; Padilha, P. & Saunders, C. (2008). Análise crítica de estudos brasileiros sobre deficiência de vitamina A no grupo materno-infantil. Revista Paulista de Pediatria, 26(4), 392-399.

Rock, C. L.; Lovaldo, J. L.; Emenhiser, C.; Ruffin, M. T.; Flatt, S. W. & Schwartz, S.J. (1998). Bioavailabity of β-carotene is lower in raw than in processed carrots and Spinachin Women. J. Nutr., 128, 913-916.

Rodrigues, R. S. M.; Penteado, M. V. C. (1989). Carotenoids with pro-vitamin A in vegetable leaves. Revista de Farmácia Bioquímica da Universidade de São Paulo. 25 (1), 39-53, 1989.

Rodriguez-Amaya, D. B. (2001). A guide to carotenoid analysis in foods. Washington, D.C.: ILSI Press.

Rodriguez-Amaya, D. B. & Kimura, M. (2004). HarvestPlus handbook for carotenoid analysis. Washinton, D.C. and Cali: HarvestPlus Technical Monograph, 2, 58p.

Rodriguez-Amaya, D. B.; Kimura, M. & Amaya-Farfan, J. (2008). Fontes brasileiras de carotenóides: tabela brasileira de composição de carotenóides em alimentos. – Brasília: MMA/SBF, 100p.

Rodriguez-Amaya, D. B.; Nutti, M. R. & Carvalho, J. L. V. (2011). Carotenoids of sweet potato, cassava, and maize and their use in bread and flour fortification. In: Preedy, R. R.; Watson, R. R.; Patel, V. B. (Eds.). Flour and breads and their fortification in health and disease prevention. London; Burlington; San Diego: Academic Press; Elsevier, chap. 28, 301-311.

Sander, L. C.; Sharpless, K. E. & Pursch, M. (2000). C30 stationary phases for the analysis of food by liquid chromatography. Journal of Chromatography A, 880, 189-202.

Sarkar, A.; Mukherjee, B.; Chatterjee, M. (1994). Inhibitory effect of β-carotene on chronic 2 acetylaminofluorene induced hepatocarcinogenesis in rat: reflection in hepatic drug metabolism. Carcinogenesis, 15 (5), 1055-1060.

Schieber, A. & Carle, R. (2005). Occurrence of carotenoid cis-isomers in food: Technological, analytical and nutricional implications. Trends in Food Science & Technology, 16, 416-422.

Seo, J. S.; Burri, B. J.; Quan, Z. & Neidlinger, T. R. (2005). Extraction and chromatography of carotenoids from pumpkin. Journal of Chromatography A, 1073, 371-375.

Setiawan, B.; Sulaeman, A.; Giraud, D. W. & Driskell, J. A. (2001). Carotenoid content of selected indonesian fruits. Journal of Food Composition and Analysis, 14, 169-176.

Silva, S. R. & Mercadante, A. Z. (2002). Carotenoid composition in yellow passion fruit (Passiflora edulis flavicarpa) in natura. Ciência e Tecnologia de Alimentos, 22(3), 254- 258.

Souza, W. A.; Boas, O. M. G. C. V. (2002). A deficiência de vitamina A no Brasil: Um panorama. Revista Panamericana de Salud Pública, 12(3), 173-179.

Stahl, W. & Sies, H. (2003). Antioxidant activity of carotenoids. Molecular Aspects of Medicine, 24 (6), 345-351.

Stahl, W. & Sies, H. (2005). Bioactivity and protective effects of natural carotenoids. Biochimica et Biophysica Acta, 1740, 101-107.

Stahl, W.; Schwarz, W.; Von Laar, J. & Sies, H. (1995). All-trans β-carotene preferentially accumulates in human chylomicrons and very low density lipoproteins compared with 9-cis geometrical isomer. Journal of Nutrition, 125, 2128-2133.

Suda, D.; Schwartz, J. & Shklar, G. (1986). Inhibition of experimental oral carcinogenesis by topical beta carotene. Carcinogenesis, 7(5), 711-715.

Tanumihardjo, S. A. (2002). Factors influencing the conversion of carotenoids to retinol: bioavailability to conversion to bioefficacy. International Journal for Vitamin and Nutrition Research, 72 (1), 40-45.

Tapiero, H.; Townsend, D. M. & Tew, K. D. (2004). The role of carotenoids in the prevention of human pathologies. Biomedicine & Pharmacotherapy, 58, 100-110.

Thakkar, S. K.; Maziya-Dixon, B.; Dixon, A. G. O. & Failla, M. L. (2007). Beta-carotene micellarization during in vitro digestion and uptake by Caco-2 cells is directly proportional to beta-carotene content in different genotypes of cassava. The Journal of Nutrition, 137, 2220- 2233.

Wada, T.; Sugatani, J.; Terada, E.; Ohguchi, M. & Miwa, M. (2005). Physicochemical characterization and biological effects of inulin enzymatically synthesized from sucrosae. J Agric. Food Chem., 53 (4), 1246-1253.

Zemplei, J.; Browman, B. B. & Russell, R. M. (2001). Present knowledge in nutrition: Biotin (10th ed.). Washington, D.C.: International Life Sciences Institute, ILSI Press. 241-252.

In: Beta-Carotene   ISBN: 978-1-62417-173-4
Editor: Maxime Lefevre   © 2013 Nova Science Publishers, Inc.

Chapter 4

APPROACHES FOR THE STABILIZATION AND ADMINISTRATION OF BETA-CAROTENE

S. Trombino, R. Cassano and T. Ferrarelli*

University of Calabria, Department of Pharmaceutical Science,
Edificio Polifunzionale, Arcavacata di Rende, Cosenza, Italy

ABSTRACT

Beta-carotene (β-carotene) has many benefits on health, in particular
it can be used to treat skin diseases, several types of cancer,
atherosclerosis, macular degeneration or to decrease oxidative stress. This
molecule is soluble in aqueous systems and sensitive to oxidation, thus its
encapsulation in appropriate drug delivery systems (DDS) might
constitute an appropriate mean to preserve its properties, increase the
solubility and enhance its physiological potencies. Various formulations
have been developed for beta-carotene limiting its exposure to high
temperature, light or oxygen. Furthermore, beta-carotene encapsulation
can lead to better efficiency allowing smaller administration doses and
consequently reducing its potential side effects. The aim of this chapter is
to examine the different formulations and techniques useful for beta-
carotene stabilization and administration.

Keywords: beta-carotene, stabilization, administration, drug delivery systems

---

* Corresponding author: Sonia Trombino; Email: sonia.trombino@unical.it; Tel: +39984493203;
Fax: +39984493298

INTRODUCTION

Carotenoids are organic pigments naturally occurring in plants and some other photosynthetic organisms. Beta-carotene is an important member of carotenoids family, found in many fruits and vegetables (carrots, sweet potato, pumpkin, papaya, star fruit, peaches, spinach, broccoli, kale, chicory and others) [1-3]. Nowadays, the major interest of beta-carotene is not only due to its provitamin A activity but also due to its antioxidant action by scavenging oxygen radicals and reducing oxidative stress in the organism [4]; thanks to these properties beta-carotene possesses preventive effects in animals and humans against many disorders like cancer, cardiovascular diseases, arteriosclerosis, macular degeneration and other age related diseases [5-8]. In addition, molecule may be also important for enhancing immune response [9], carcinogen-metabolizing enzyme activity [10] and regulating cell growth [11-13]. In spite of a wide range of biological and pharmacological effects, the applications of beta-carotene are still limited due to its instability. In fact, beta-carotene and the other carotenoids are oxidized by light and heat exposure due to the presence of conjugated double bonds in their molecules (Figure 1).

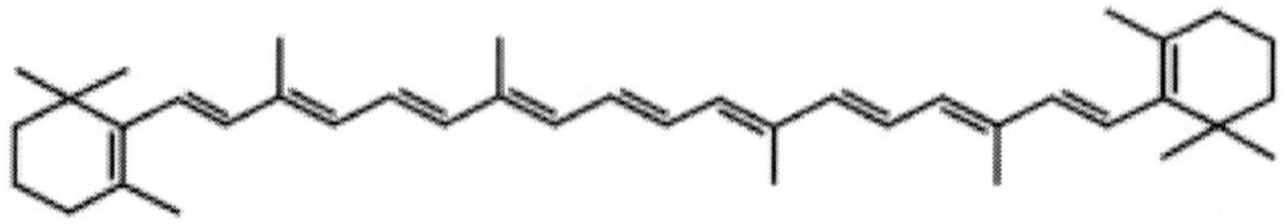

Figure 1. β-carotene structure.

Another specificity of this compound is its high hydrophobicity that makes it insoluble in aqueous systems and therefore poorly available and for this reason beta-carotene requires solubilization by bile salts, chylomicrons or lipoproteins in order to be transported in the human body [14].

The purpose of this chapter is to focus on the strategies adopted to increase carotenoids solubility and stability such as incorporation into nanofibers, nanoparticles, emulsions, niosomes or techniques such as microencapsulation and spray-drying that can offer promising means of improving beta-carotene bioavailability.

ELECTROSPUN ZEIN FIBERS

Nanofibers are submicron sized fibers with average diameters in sub-micrometer down to nanometer range, obtained through an electrospinning process (Figure 2) [15], that exhibit several interesting characteristics such as a high surface area to mass or volume ratio, a small inter-fibrous pore size with high porosity, vast possibilities for surface functionalization, etc. [16].

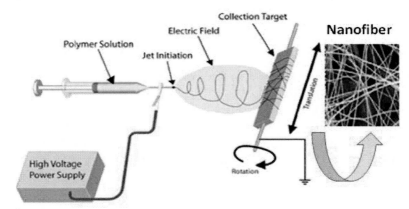

Adapted with correction from reference 15.

Figure 2. Schematic representation of electrospinning process.

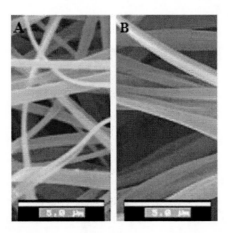

Figure 3. SEM images of electrospun fiber mats of zein (A) and zein with β-carotene (B) (Adapted with correction from reference 17)

Zein is a biodegradable and sustainable material with great potential in the replacement of traditional oil-based plastics. Zein originates from renewable resources and it is still finding many commercial applications due to its excellent film forming properties; it is also being used with significant interest as a textile fiber and in coatings, for example, in food or pharmaceutical industries [17]. In 2009 Fernandez *et al.* encapsulated beta-carotene in zein ultrafine fibers (Figure 3) and as a result, the molecule showed a remarkably good protection against oxidation and a significant increase in the light stability when exposed to UV–vis irradiation [18].

SOLID LIPID NANOPARTICLES AND NANOSTRUCTURED LIPID CARRIERS

Solid Lipid Nanoparticles (SLNs) are nanoparticles with a solid lipid matrix and an average diameter in the nanometer range. Common ingredients include solid lipids, emulsifiers and water. Lipids comprise triglycerides, partial glycerides, fatty acids, steroids, and waxes (Figure 4).

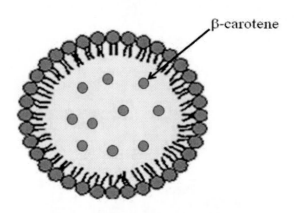

Figure 4. Schematic representation of Solid Lipid Nanoparticles (SLN) containing β-carotene.

As reported by Pardeike and others [19], a solid lipid carrier, incorporating a labile bioactive molecule, may improve its stability thanks to the limited diffusion of reactive species (for example, oxygen) through the solid matrix, as demonstrated for solid lipid nanoparticles containing retinol.

For this reason Trombino *et al.* developed stearyl ferulate-based solid lipid nanoparticles (SF-SLNs), as vehicle for both β-carotene and α-tocopherol, with the aim to increase the photochemical stability of these compounds [20]. Ferulic acid was introduced in these formulations because it is a potent antioxidant acting in synergy with other antioxidants being able to protect and stabilize them from degradation [21]. The obtained SF-SLNs represent a good vehicle for β-carotene as they are able to stabilize it and to prevent its oxidation and degradation. In 2009 Helgason and co-workers investigated the impact of surfactant type on physical and chemical stability of solid lipid nanoparticle (SLN) suspensions loading β-carotene [22]. In particular, the role of the surfactant was investigated using aqueous phases containing different water-soluble surfactants such as high-melting (HM) lecithin, low-melting (LM) lecithin, Tween 60, Tween 80 and taurodeoxycholate as cosurfactant. In addition, the impact of the physical state of the lipidic carrier was investigated by using either a high melting point lipid (tripalmitin), to form solid particles, or a low melting point lipid (medium chain triglycerides, MCT), to form liquid droplets. With the exception of the HM-lecithin-coated solid particles, the suspensions were stable to particle aggregation during 21 days of storage. β-Carotene degradation after 21 days of storage was 11, 97, 100, and 91% in the solid particles (tripalmitin) and 16, 21, 95, and 90% in the liquid droplets (MCT) for HM-lecithin, LM-lecithin, Tween 80, and Tween 60, respectively. The results suggested that β-carotene may be stabilized by LM- or HM-lecithin when liquid carrier lipids are used and by HM-lecithin when solid carrier lipids are used. This effect is attributed to the impact of the surfactant tails on the generation of a crystal structure better suited to maintain the chemical stability of the encapsulated bioactive compound. Hentschel *et al.* obtained β-carotene-loaded nanostructured lipid carriers (NLC) [23]. NLC are a type of lipid nanoparticles with a particle matrix consisting in a blend of a liquid and solid lipid. As a consequence, NLC suspensions contain much less water than SLN suspensions. They produced these particles by melting the lipid blend at 80 °C and dispersing it into a hot emulsifier solution.

Aggregation of the dispersion particles stored at temperature of 4 until to 8 °C was not observed in the investigation period of 30 week, which shows evidence of good stability. The small particle size of around 400 nm offers the possibility to use NLC as a food colloid in several applications. In addition, the investigated model system shows increased protection against degradation of fine water dispersed β-carotene inside the particles when tocopherol was added, but poor β-carotene stability without tocopherol and in diluted solution.

More recently Lacatusu *et al.* explored the potential of two natural oils (squalene-Sq and grape seed oil-GSO) to prepare biocompatible antioxidant nanostructured lipid carriers-NLCs as a safety and protective formulation for sensitive β-carotene [24]. Particularly Lacatusu and co-workers prepared different oil-in-water nanoemulsions stabilized by a combination of alkylpolyoxy ethylene sorbitans, lecithin and a block copolymer, using a melt high-shear homogenization process. The developed carotene-NLCs presented an excellent physical stability. Furthermore, the carotene-NLCs have been evaluated in terms of *in vitro* antioxidant properties. The presence of Sq and GSO produced a significant effect on the antioxidant capacity of developed NLCs. The samples prepared with GSO and Tween 80 as main surfactant showed the highest antioxidant activity against free oxygen radicals, exhibiting an enhancement of 35% for loaded NLCs, in comparison to pure carotene.

NIOSOMES

Niosomes are microscopic lamellar structures (Figure 5), which are formed on the admixture of non-ionic surfactant of the alkyl or dialkyl polyglycerol ether class and cholesterol with subsequent hydration in aqueous media [25]. Structurally, niosomes are similar to widely studied phospholipid vesicles (liposomes), in that they are also made up of a bilayer. However, the bilayer in the case of niosomes is made up of non-ionic surface active agents rather than phospholipids as seen in the case of liposomes. Most surface active agents, when immersed in water, yield micellar structures. However, some surfactants can yield bilayer vesicles which are niosomes.

Niosomes have recently been shown to greatly increase transdermal drug delivery of drugs and they can be also used in targeted drug delivery.

In 2005 Palozza et al. co-workers developed a niosomal formulation able to solubilize, stabilize and deliver beta-carotene at physiologically relevant concentrations to cultured cells [14]. As a comparative system, the effects of β-carotene solubilized in the commonly used solvent THF [26, 27] were also studied. The stability of β-carotene in niosomes and in THF solution was compared at the same concentration of 20 μM, which represents the maximum one achievable in niosomal preparation. The results showed that β-carotene in THF was much less stable than in niosomes. These results were obtained when carotenoid stability was tested at 50 °C in the light and in the dark under air. Moreover, β-carotene was much more stable under nitrogen (no air) than under

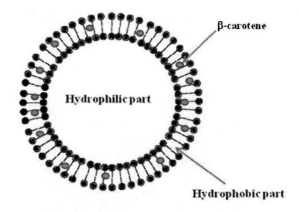

Figure 5. Schematic representation of niosome containing β-carotene.

air, although such stability was much higher in niosomes than in THF. The different stability of β-carotene became extremely remarkable when carotenoid was maintained in polystyrene, the most used material for cell cultures, rather than in glass containers. Also in this case, carotenoid was much more stable in niosomes than in THF solution. After all β-carotene formulations, in THF solution and in niosomes, were also exposed to different free radical generators such as AAPH (2,2'-azobis(2-amidino-propane) dihydrochloride) and H_2O_2 (hydrogen peroxide). In both the cases, an enhanced carotenoid stability in niosomes compared to THF solution was observed. The study showed that niosomes are able to stabilize β-carotene by preventing its oxidation and degradation and that β-carotene niosomal formulation may be taken up by cultured cells at concentrations spanning the range of physiological levels.

EMULSIONS AND NANOMULSIONS

An emulsion is a system in which one fluid is dispersed in another immiscible one. Macroscopic separation of the phases is prevented by the addition of a suitable surfactant. In the vast majority of emulsion research, one of the liquid phases is water [28].

A nanoemulsion is a submicron thermodynamically stable isotropically clear dispersion of two immiscible liquids, such as oil and water, stabilized by an interfacial film of surfactant molecules. In particular, it is considered to be a thermodynamically or kinetically stable liquid dispersion of an oil phase and a water phase, in combination with a surfactant. The dispersed phase typically comprises small particles or droplets, with a size range of 5 nm-200 nm (Figure 6), and has very low oil/water interfacial tension [28].

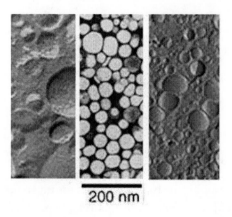

Figure 6. Transmission electron micrography (TEM) of various nanoemulsions.

On the basis of their composition we distinguish three types of emulsion or nanoemulsions:

- Oil in water (O/W) wherein oil droplets are dispersed in the continuous aqueous phase
- Water in oil (W/O) wherein water droplets are dispersed in the continuous oil phase;
- Bi-continuous wherein microdomains of oil and water are interdispersed within the system.

Both emulsions and nanoemulsions [29] are under extensive investigation as drug carriers for improving therapeutic agents delivery.

Cornacchia and Roos included β-carotene in the dispersed phase of conventional O/W emulsions stabilized by various concentrations of whey protein isolate (WPI) [30]. Emulsions were thermally treated to produce 2 sets of systems with identical composition but different physical states of the lipid carrier (solid lipid particles, SLP, and liquid lipid particles, LLP). Kinetics of β-carotene degradation during isothermal storage was studied, and the possible differences in stabilization efficacy of solid and liquid particles and interface structure were determined. This gave indications of possible strategies for an enhanced stability of labile functional liposoluble compounds included in improved food formulations.

In 2007 Yuan *et al.* prepared and charcterized β-carotene O/W nanoemulsions obtained by high pressure homogenization using a series of polyoxythylene sorbitan esters of fatty acids as emulsifiers [31]. The influence of the emulsifier type and concentration, as well as the homogenization conditions of pressure, temperature and cycle on the physicochemical properties of the nanoemulsions was systematically examined using a dynamic light scattering (DLS) technique. The nanoemulsions stability and their content in β-carotene during storage were monitored for a period of four weeks. The results showed that β-carotene nanoemulsions had good physical stabilities but, chemically, significant degradation of β-carotene occurred during storage.

POLYLACTIC ACID NANOPARTICLES

Another strategy to increase β-carotene stability is its encapsulation into polylactic acid (PLA) nanoparticles [32]. PLA is a biodegradable polymer (Figure 6) derived from renewable resources which is recognised as safe (GRAS) and is of great interest in food applications because of its potentially useful physical and mechanical characteristics [33].

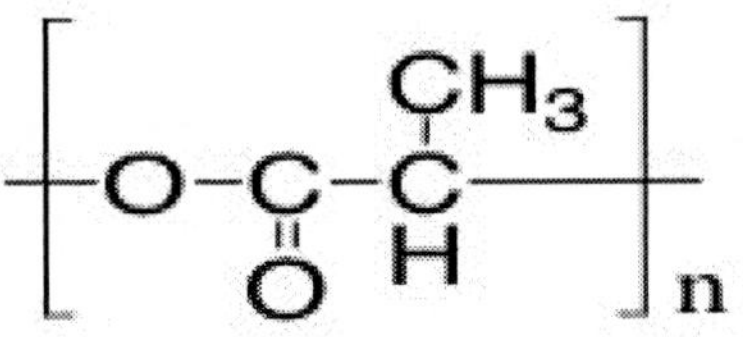

Figure 7. Structure of polylactic acid (PLA).

In their study Cao-Hoang and co-workers [32], investigated the oxidation of β-carotene, from synthetic and natural origins, after dispersion in Tween micelles or poly lactic acid (PLA) particles. Two oxidation systems were used: autooxidation and oxidation by xanthine oxidase-generated-reactive oxygen species. The results showed that in comparison with dispersion in Tween micelles, the encapsulation of β-carotene in polylactic acid particles gives rise to a more stable supramolecular organization which offers better protection against oxidation, thus resulting in less prooxidating compounds upon degradation. For the beta-carotene sample which has been pre-oxidized prior to encapsulation, as it is likely to occur during extraction from natural materials, dispersion is more difficult since the sample already contained some oxidation products, consequently leading to a decrease in the encapsulation efficiency. PLA encapsulation is particularly interesting in such cases as it would permit a reduction in the prooxidizing product contents of the sample.

MICROENCAPSULATION

A solution to prevent carotenoid oxidation and isomerization is the use of microencapsulation, a technique commonly used to increase carotenoids stability [6, 34].

Microencapsulation is the technique by which the sensitive ingredients are packed within a coating or wall material (Figure 8).

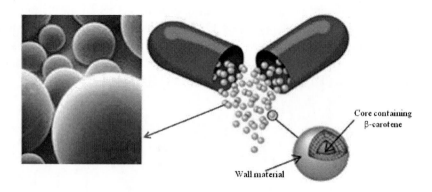

Figure 8. Schematic representation of microencapsulation.

The wall material protects the sensitive ingredient against adverse reactions (oxygen, light), prevents the loss of volatile ingredients and controls their release [35]. The capsule is very small in size, approximately 5–300 micron in diameter [36] It can consist of a continuous core region surrounded by a continuous shell or it can have irregular geometry consisting of small particles of core material dispersed in a matrix of shell material [37]. Different wall materials are used in food industry such as gums, celluloses, starches and proteins [38]. Spada *et al.* produced and characterized microcapsules containing β-carotene as core material and using native pinhao starch, hydrolysed pinhao starch 6 dextrose equivalent (DE), hydrolysed pinhao starch 12 DE and the mixture of these materials with gelatin as coating material [39]. The purpose the research was to produce and characterize these microcapsules. The capsules efficiency, surface content, moisture, morphology, solubility, particle size and glass transition temperature were analysed. The hydrolysed pinhao starch 12 DE showed the highest total β-carotene content and the lowest surface β-carotene content, unlike the native starch. Using scanning electron microscopy, it was observed that all microcapsules presented undefined shapes. The samples with gelatin had wider particle size distribution, higher diameters, lower solubility and higher glass transition temperature when compared with other samples. Results obtained suggest that the modified pinhao starch can be considered as potential wall material for encapsulation of β-carotene.

FURCELLARAN BEADS

Furcellaran is an anionic sulphated polysaccharide extracted from the red algae *Furcellaria lumbricalis* [40]. Furcellaran is a copolymer of β- and κ-carrageenan [41] and is usually represented as a structurally repeating unit of alternating 3-linked β-d-galactopyranose and 4-linked α-d-galactopyranose residues (Figure 8), with a part of the latter existing as a 3,6-anhydro derivative [42].

Furcellaran forms gels, undergoing a transition from coil (disordered sol state) to helix (ordered state) transition, triggered by a reduction in temperature and/or through ionic interactions. Being a nontoxic, biodegradable, biocompatible polysaccharide, furcellaran is a very promising biomaterial for encapsulation. For this reason Laos *et al.* prepared furcellaran beads entrapping β-carotene [40]. Beads were prepared by ionotropic gelation. The influence of bead formulation factors on the particle size and firmness was investigated and the encapsulation efficiency of β-carotene in beads was studied. The nature of the cation, the polymer and cation concentration, and the proportion of volumes of the outer to the inner phase influenced the size and firmness of furcellaran beads. With increasing proportion of sea buckthorn juice in the formulae, firmness of furcellaran beads decreased. The encapsulation efficiency of β-carotene from sea buckthorn juice in furcellaran capsules was 97%. It suggested that furcellaran beads may be applied for β-carotene encapsulation.

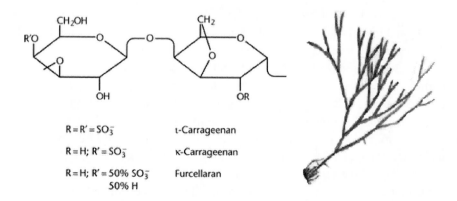

Figure 9. Schematic representation of furcelleran.

REFERENCES

[1]   Rodriguez-Amaya, D.B. (2002). A Scheme for obtaining standards and HPLC quantifcation of leafy vegetable carotenoids. *Food Chemistry. 78, 389.*

[2]   Chandrika, U.G., Jansz, E.R., Wickramasinghe, S.N. & Warnasuriya, N.D. (2003). Carotenoids in yellow- and red-fleshed papaya (*Carica papaya L*). *Journal of Science and Food and Agriculture. 83, 1279.*

[3]   Kandlakunta, B., Rajendran, A. & Thingnganing, L. (2008). Carotene content of some common (cereals, pulses, vegetables, spices and condiments) and unconventional sources of plant origin. *Food Chemistry. 106, 85.*

[4]   Young, A.J. & Lowe, G.M. (2001). Antioxidant and prooxidant properties of carotenoids. Archives of Biochemistry and Biophysics *385, 20.*

[5]   Gonnet M., Lethuaut L., Boury F. (2010).New trends in encapsulation of liposoluble vitamins Journal of Controlled Release *146, 276.*

[6]   Laos K., Lõugas T., Mändmets A., Vokk R. (2007). Encapsulation of β-carotene from sea buckthorn (Hippophaë rhamnoides L.) juice in furcellaran beads. *Innovative Food Science and Emerging Technologies 8, 395.*

[7]   Mayne, S.T. (1996). Beta-carotene, carotenoids and disease prevention in humans. *FASEB J. 10, 690.*

[8]   Ziegler, R.G., Mayne, S.T., Swanson, C.A. (1996). Nutrition and lung cancer. *Cancer Causes Control 7, 157.*

[9]   Bendich, A., (1989). Carotenoids and the immune response. *J. Nutr. 119, 112.*

[10] Astorg, P., Gradelet, S., Berges, R., Suschetet, M., (1996). No evidence for an inhibitory effect of beta-carotene or of canthaxanthin on the initiation of liver preneoplastic foci by diethylnitrosamine in the rat. *Nutr. Cancer 25, 27.*

[11] Palozza, P., Serini, S., Di Nicuolo, F., Calviello, G., (2001). Mitogenic and apoptotic signaling by carotenoids: involvement of a redox mechanism. *IUBMB Life 52, 77.*

[12] Palozza, P., Serini, S., Di Nicuolo, F., Calviello, G., (2004a). Modulation of apoptotic signalling by carotenoids in cancer cells. *Arch. Biochem. Biophys. 430, 104.*

[13] Palozza, P., Serini, S., Di Nicuolo, F., Boninsegna, A., Torsello, A., Maggiano, N., Ranelletti, F.O., Wolf, F.I., Calviello, G., Cittadini, A., (2004b). Beta-carotene exacerbates DNA oxidative damage and modifies p53-related pathways of cell proliferation and apoptosis in cultured cells exposed to tobacco smoke condensate. *Carcinogenesis 25, 1.*

[14] Palozza, P., Muzzalupo, R., Trombino, S., Valdannini, A., Picci, N. (2006). Solubilization and stabilization of beta-carotene in niosomes: delivery to cultured cells. *Chemistry and Physics of Lipids, 139, 32.*

[15] Trombino S. (2012). Strategies for vitamin E transdermal delivery, In: Handbook of diet, nutrition and the skin. By Preedy V. Wageningen Academic Publishers. *8, 129.*

[16] Deitzel, J.M., Kleinmeyer, J., Harris, D., Beck, Tan, N.C., (2001). The effect of processing variables on the morphology of electrospun nanofibers and textiles. *Polymer 42, 261.*

[17] Shukla, R., & Cheryan, M. (2001). Zein: the industrial protein from corn. *Industrial Crops and Products, 13, 171.*

[18] Fernandez A.,Torres-Giner S., Lagaron J.M. (2009). Novel route to stabilization of bioactive antioxidant by encapsulation in electrospun fibers of zein prolamine. *Food Hydrocolloids. 23,1427.*

[19] Pardeike J, Hommoss A, Muller RH. (2009). Lipid nanoparticles (SLN, NLC) in cosmetic and pharmaceutical dermal products. *Int J Pharmaceutics 366,170.*

[20] Trombino S., Cassano R., Muzzalupo R., Pingitore A., Cione E., Picci N. (2009). Stearyl ferulate-based solid lipid nanoparticles for the

encapsulation and stabilization of b-carotene and a-tocopherol. *Colloids and Surfaces B: Biointerfaces 72, 181.*

[21] Trombino S., Serini S., Di Nicuolo F., Celleno L., Andò S., Picci N., Calviello G., Palozza P. (2004). Antioxidant effect of ferulic acid in isolated membranes and intact cells: synergistic interactions with alfa-tocopherol, beta-carotene and ascorbic acid *J. Agric. Food Chem. 52, 2411.*

[22] Helgason T., Awad T.S., Kristbergsson K., Decker E.A., McClements D.J. Weiss J. (2009) Impact of Surfactant Properties on Oxidative Stability of β-Carotene Encapsulated within Solid Lipid Nanoparticles. *J. Agric. Food Chem. 57, 8033.*

[23] Hentschel A., Gramdorf S., Muller R.H., Kurz T. (2008). β-Carotene-Loaded Nanostructured Lipid Carriers. *Journal of Food Science. 73, 2.*

[24] Lacatusu I., Badea N., Ovidiu O., Bojin D., Meghea A. (2012) Highly antioxidant carotene-lipid nanocarriers: synthesis and antibacterial activity. *Journal Nanoparticle Research. 14, 902.*

[25] Malhotra M. and Jain N.K. (1994). Niosomes as Drug Carriers. *Indian Drugs, 31, 81.*

[26] Bertram, J.S., Pung, A., Churley, M., Kappock, T.J., Wilkins, L.R., Cooney, R.V., (1991). Diverse carotenoids protect against chemicallyinduced neoplastic transformation. *Carcinogenesis 12, 671.*

[27] Scita, G., Aponte, G.W., Wolf, G., (1992). Uptake and cleavage of β-carotene by cultures of rat small intestinal cells and human lung fibroblasts. *J. Nutr. Biochem. 3, 118.*

[28] Devarajan V. and Ravichandran V., (2011) Nanoemulsions: as modified drug delivery tool. *Pharmacie Globale. (IJCP) 2, 1.*

[29] Shah P., Bhalodia D., Shelat P., (2010) Nanoemulsion: A pharmaceutical review. *Sys Rev. Pharm. 1, 24.*

[30] Cornacchia L. and Roos Y. H., (2011). State of Dispersed Lipid Carrier and Interface Composition as Determinants of Beta-Carotene Stability in Oil-in-Water Emulsions, *Journal of Food Science, 76, 1211.*

[31] Yuan Y., Gao Y., Zhao J., Mao L. (2008). Characterization and stability evaluation of b-carotenenanoemulsions prepared by high pressure homogenization under various emulsifying conditions. *Food Research International 41, 61.*

[32] Cao-Hoang L., Fougere R., Wache Y. (2011). Increase in stability and change in supramolecular structure of b-carotene through encapsulation into polylactic acid nanoparticles. *Food Chemistry 124, 42.*

[33] Jin, T., Zhang, H. (2008). Biodegradable polylactic acid polymer with nisin for use in antimicrobial food packaging. *Journal of Food Science, 73, 127.*

[34] Loksuwan, J. (2007). Characteristics of microencapsulated b carotene formed by spray drying with modified tapioca starch, native tapioca starch and maltodextrin. *Food Hydrocolloids, 21, 928.*

[35] Vos, P., Faas, M., Spasojevic, M. & Sikkema, J. (2010). Encapsulation for preservation of functionality and targeted delivery of bioactive food components. *International Dairy Journal, 20, 292.*

[36] Gibbs, B. F., Kermash, S., Alli, I. and Mulligan, C. N. 1999. Encapsulation in the food industry: a review. *International Journal of Food Sciences and Nutrition, 50, 213.*

[37] Vilstrup, P. Ed. 2001. Microencapsulation of food ingredients. Leatherhead Publishing. LFRA, Leatherhead, England.

[38] Jackson, L.S. & Lee, K. (1991). Microencapsulation and food industry. LWT -*Food Science and Technology, 24, 289.*

[39] Spada J. C., Ferreira Marczak L. D., Tessaro I. C., Zapata C. (2012) Microencapsulation of β-carotene using native pinhao starch, modified pinhao starch and gelatin by freeze-drying. *International Journal of Food Science and Technology, 47,186.*

[40] Laos K., Lõugas T., Mändmets A., Vokk R. (2007). Encapsulation of β-carotene from sea buckthorn (Hippophaë rhamnoides L.) juice in furcellaran beads. *Innovative Food Science and Emerging Technologies. 8, 395.*

[41] Hugerth, A., Sundelöf, L. O. (2001). The effect of polyelectrolyte counterion specificity, charge density, and conformation on polyelectrolyte–amphiphile interaction: The carrageenan/furcellaran–amitriptyline system. *Biopolymers, 58, 186.*

[42] Glicksman, M. (1984). Carrageenans. In M. Glicksman (Ed.), New York: CRC Press. *Food hydrocolloids. 83.*

In: Beta-Carotene   ISBN: 978-1-62417-173-4
Editor: Maxime Lefevre   © 2013 Nova Science Publishers, Inc.

Chapter 5

EFFECTS OF DIETARY BETA-CAROTENE ON LUNG FUNCTION, RESPIRATORY SYMPTOMS AND CHRONIC OBSTRUCTIVE PULMONARY DISEASE

Andy H. Lee[*]

School of Public Health, Curtin University, Perth, WA, Australia

ABSTRACT

This chapter reviews the epidemiological evidence on the effects of dietary beta-carotene on lung function, respiratory symptoms, mortality and risk of developing chronic obstructive pulmonary disease (COPD). Published studies are located by searching several electronic databases using the relevant key words. High levels of intake of beta-carotene were found to improve lung function (forced expiratory volume in one second and forced vital capacity) and appeared to have some protective effects against respiratory symptoms such as dyspnea, cough and excessive phlegm. However, no tentative conclusion on the association between dietary beta-carotene and both the risk and mortality of COPD can be drawn. In view of the emerging epidemiological evidence, further clinical

---

[*] Corresponding autor: Professor Andy H. Lee, PhD, School of Public Health, Curtin Health Innovation Research Institute, Curtin University, GPO Box U 1987, Perth, WA, 6845, Australia, Phone: 61-8-92664180, Fax: 61-8-92662958 Email: Andy.Lee@curtin.edu.au.

and experimental research is required to ascertain the role of beta-carotene on the aetiology of COPD.

Keywords: Antioxidant, dietary beta-carotene, lung function, respiratory symptoms, vitamin

DIETARY BETA-CAROTENE

Beta-carotene is a carotenoid compound responsible for giving fruits and vegetables their orange pigment. The main sources of dietary beta-carotene from vegetables include carrot, sweet potato, pumpkin, butternut squash, spinach, kale, turnip greens, lettuce and collard. Fruits such as mango, cantaloupe and apricot are also high in beta-carotene. Being a powerful antioxidant, beta-carotene is a fat soluble vitamin that can protect the lungs from oxidative damage resulting from smoking or air pollution [1]. Antioxidant mechanisms involve any cell process that prevents the formation of free radicals, converts oxidants to less toxic species, directs reactive species away from vital cellular structures, or repairs oxidant injury. It is known that antioxidant enzymes form a first line of defense in the lungs. Uric acid and the antioxidants including beta-carotene from diet form a second line of defense [2].

CHRONIC OBSTRUCTIVE PULMONARY DISEASE

Chronic Obstructive Pulmonary Disease (COPD) is a systemic and disabling pathological condition with a progressive course, characterized by lung function impairment with not fully reversible airflow limitation. It represents a major health problem worldwide. Patients with COPD have symptoms that include chronic cough, sputum production, and dyspnea on exertion [3-5]. COPD is now the fifth most common cause of morbidity in the world and will be the third leading cause of death by 2020 [6]. Cigarette smoking is established as the principal risk factor [3-5]. Although 95% of COPD patients are, or have been, cigarette smokers, about 20% of smokers develop COPD [7]. Therefore, apart from tobacco abstinence, other lifestyle and environmental factors may protect against or contribute to the development of this disease. Because of the high burden and societal cost associated with COPD, studies on new methods of prevention, especially lifestyle modifiable factors, are important.

A literature review of dietary factors suggested that fruit intake is positively associated with lung function but inversely related to COPD mortality and respiratory symptoms. Increased vegetable consumption can also reduce the risk of COPD, whereas a high fish intake is beneficial to lung function [8]. The emphasis in the literature has placed on foods and dietary patterns rather than individual nutrients. In the present review, epidemiological evidence of the effects of beta-carotene on COPD in terms of lung function, respiratory symptoms, mortality and risk of development are discussed. Some tentative conclusions are made concerning the role of beta-carotene in the aetiology of COPD.

LITERATURE SEARCH

Published articles were located by searching the PubMed, CINAHL, ProQuest and Web of Science databases using key words 'beta-carotene', 'lung function', 'respiratory symptom', and 'chronic obstructive pulmonary disease', without any restriction on publication date. Article reference lists were also searched for relevant papers. A total of 9 articles were assessed as being relevant to the present review of epidemiological evidence for COPD, whereas intervention studies and experimental clinical trials were excluded. These comprised 6 articles for beta-carotene and 3 review articles, some of them overlapping on the topics. This review of epidemiologic studies focuses on dietary beta-carotene from foods rather than dietary supplements whose consumptions are not directly comparable. Table 1 summarizes the literature findings concerning the effects of beta-carotene on lung function, COPD risk, COPD mortality and respiratory symptoms.

LUNG FUNCTION

A large cross-sectional study of 6555 Dutch adults aged 20-59 years was undertaken to investigate the relationships between lung function and the intake of antioxidants including beta-carotene [9].

Table 1. Dietary beta-carotene and lung function, COPD risk, COPD mortality and respiratory symptoms

Country	Study population and design	Dietary assessment instrument	Level of intake	Results	Reference
Lung function				Change in lung function (95% CI)	
The Netherlands	6555 adults, aged 20-59 years, cross-sectional study	Semi-quantitative food frequency questionnaire	Highest versus lowest quintiles	60 (31 to 89) ml higher in FEV1 and 75 (40 to 110) ml higher in FVC	[9]
Finland, Italy, The Netherlands	1248 men in Finland, 1386 men in Italy, 691 men in the Netherlands, aged 40-59 years, cross-sectional study	Cross-check dietary history method	Highest versus lowest tertiles	141 (27 to 255) ml higher in FEV1 in the Netherlands No significant change in FEV1 in Finland and Italy	[10]
COPD risk				Adjusted odds ratio (95% CI)	
Japan	278 patients with COPD, 340 community-based controls, case-control study	Semi-quantitative food frequency questionnaire	Highest versus lowest quartiles	0.61 (0.33 to 1.13)	[12]

Country	Study population and design	Dietary assessment instrument	Level of intake	Results	Reference
COPD mortality				Adjusted risk ratio (95% CI)	
Finland, Italy, Greece, Japan, US, Serbia, former Yugoslavia	12763 men, aged 40-59 years, population-based cohort study, 25-year follow-up	7-day record method	10% increase in mean intake of 2 mg/day	1.01 (0.94 to 1.08)	[13]
Finland, Italy, The Netherlands	2917 men, aged 50-69 years, prospective study, 20-year follow-up	Cross-check dietary history method	Highest versus lowest tertiles	0.75 (0.42 to 1.34)	[14]
Respiratory symptoms				Adjusted odds ratio (95% CI)	
The Netherlands	6555 adults, aged 20-59 years, cross-sectional study	Semi-quantitative food frequency questionnaire	Highest versus lowest quintiles	1.27 (1.04 to 1.55) for wheeze	[9]
US	29133 male smokers, aged 50-69 years, cohort study, 6-year follow-up	Food use questionnaire	Highest versus lowest tertiles	0.75 (0.71 to 0.80) for cough 0.82 (0.77 to 0.87) for phlegm 0.67 (0.62 to 0.71) for dyspnea 0.78 (0.73 to 0.83) for chronic bronchitis	[15]

Dietary intake was assessed by a semi-quantitative food frequency questionnaire. The mean beta-carotene intake was 2.3 mg/day (SD 1.1).

Subjects at the highest level of intake had a 60 ml (95% confidence interval (CI) 31 to 89) increase in forced expiratory volume in one second (FEV1) and 75 ml (95% CI 40 to 110) increase in forced vital capacity (FVC) than those with a low intake of beta-carotene [9]. Another cross-sectional study collected dietary intake data using the cross-check dietary history method from three European countries (Finland, 1248 men; Italy, 1386 men; the Netherlands, 691 men). FEV1 was measured by spirometry [10]. While no significant change in FEV1 was observed in Finland and Italy, the Dutch men with mean beta-carotene intake of 1.1 mg (SD 0.4) reported a difference of 141 ml (95% CI 27 to 255) in FEV1 between the highest and lowest level of beta-carotene intake [10]. Therefore, such associations between beta-carotene and pulmonary function were not consistent across countries.

RISK OF COPD

Very few investigations of dietary nutrients such as beta-carotene in relation to COPD risk and COPD mortality have been undertaken, because large-scale epidemiological studies especially long-term prospective cohort studies are often difficult to conduct due to time and cost constraints. So far, only preliminary findings are available [11]. A case-control study was conducted in central Japan in 2006 [12].

A total of 278 patients with COPD diagnosed within the past four years and 340 community-based controls were recruited and interviewed face-to-face. Habitual food consumption data were obtained using a validated 138-item semi-quantitative food frequency questionnaire developed for the Japanese adult population. The reference recall for dietary variables was set at five years before interview.

The main nutrients and antioxidants derived from vegetables and fruits were then identified and estimated from all foods using the Japanese food composition tables. Effects of selected nutrients on the COPD risk were then assessed by separate logistic regression models adjusting for demographic and lifestyle confounding factors and total energy intake. High levels of beta-carotene intake ($\geq$ 3055µg per day) appeared to reduce the risk of COPD (adjusted odds ratio (OR) 0.61, 95% CI 0.33 to 1.13), but the reduction was not significant with p = 0.184 [12].

COPD MORTALITY

A large population-based cohort study involving 12763 men aged 40-59 years from seven countries (Finland, Italy, Greece, Japan, US, Serbia, former Yugoslavia) used information collected on baseline diet to perform ecological analysis of the COPD mortality rate [13]. After 25 years of follow-up, no association between beta-carotene intake and COPD mortality was found. The COPD mortality rate ratio, for a 10% increase in mean beta-carotene intake of 0.2 mg/day, was 1.01 (95% CI 0.94 to 1.08) adjusting for total energy intake. Similarly, another population-based prospective study investigated the relation between baseline antioxidant intake (including beta-carotene) and 20 year COPD mortality among 2917 men aged 50-69 years from three European countries, namely, Finland, Italy, and the Netherlands [14]. Baseline information on diet was collected using the cross-check dietary history method. Again, no significant effect on mortality rate was observed for beta-carotene. The rate ratio was 0.75 (95% CI 0.42 to 1.34) for the highest (> 1.4 mg/day) versus lowest (< 0.9 mg/day) of baseline beta-carotene intake, after adjustment for age, smoking and country [14].

RESPIRATORY SYMPTOMS

A large cohort study of 29133 male smokers aged 50-69 years in the US examined the baseline prevalences of respiratory symptoms in relation to the dietary intakes of beta-carotene, retinol and vitamin E. The dietary data were collected using a food use questionnaire. High dietary intake of beta-carotene (> 2.3 mg/day) appeared to be beneficial against cough (OR 0.75, 95% CI 0.71 to 0.80), phlegm (OR 0.82, 95% CI 0.77 to 0.87), dyspnea (OR 0.67, 95% CI 0.62 to 0.71) and chronic bronchitis (OR 0.78, 95% CI 0.73 to 0.83) when compared to the lowest level of intake (< 1.2 mg/day) [15]. On the contrary, dietary beta-carotene was considered a risk factor for wheeze (OR 1.27, 95% CI 1.04 to 1.55) among 6555 Dutch adults aged 20-59 years in a cross-sectional study using a self-administered questionnaire, even though its intake was not associated with most respiratory symptoms like cough, phlegm, productive cough and shortness of breath [9]. Therefore, results of the effect of beta-carotene on respiratory symptoms are inconsistent. Unlike objective measures of lung function, self-reported respiratory symptoms are rather subjective and patients may not aware of any significant changes over time.

CONCLUSION AND RECOMMENDATION

The present review considered the epidemiological evidence from six cross-sectional and prospective cohort studies. Based on the available evidence and three separate reviews [2, 11, 16] it appears that beta-carotene may improve lung function and offer some protective effects against respiratory symptoms. However, in view of the limited results, no tentative conclusion on the association between dietary beta-carotene and both the risk and mortality of COPD can be drawn.

Although the current study of epidemiological evidence is neither a systematic review nor a meta-analysis, the inherent publication bias may influence the results and the magnitude of effects of beat-carotene, especially since the studied populations are quite different in terms of demographic, lifestyle and clinical characteristics. Further research is required to ascertain the role of beta-carotene on the aetiology of COPD. Two streams of research are envisaged. Firstly, case-control and prospective cohort studies of beta-carotene would provide important epidemiological evidence of its effects on the risk and mortality of COPD. These can take place in different countries with different dietary intake and food consumption patterns. Meta-analyses of the resulting pooled data would also give useful insights to clarify its relationship with the disease development and survival. Secondly, experimental clinical trials and animal studies of dietary beta-carotene supplements will complement and provide additional supporting evidence. The increase in knowledge should be beneficial for the prevention and treatment of COPD.

REFERENCES

[1]   Smit, H. A., Grievink, L., Tabak, C. Dietary influences on chronic obstructive lung disease and asthma: a review of the epidemiological evidence. *Proc. Nutr. Soc.* 1999; 58: 309-319.

[2]   Grievink, L., Smit, H. A., Brunekreef, B. Anti-oxidants and air pollution in relation to indicators of asthma and COPD: a review of the current evidence. *Clin. and Experimental Allergy* 2000; 30: 1344-1354.

[3]   McKenzie, D. K., Frith, P. A., Burdon, J. G., Town, G. I. The COPDX Plan: Australian and New Zealand Guidelines for the management of

Chronic Obstructive Pulmonary Disease 2003. *Med. J. Aust.* 2003; 178: S7-S39.

[4]   Celli, B. R., MacNee, W. Standards for the diagnosis and treatment of patients with COPD: a summary of the ATS/ERS position paper. *Eur. Respir. J.* 2004; 23: 932-946.

[5]   Pauwels, R. A., Rabe, K. F. Burden and clinical features of chronic obstructive pulmonary disease (COPD). *Lancet* 2004; 364: 613-620.

[6]   Murray, C. J., Lopez, A. D. Alternative projections of mortality and disability by cause 1990-2020: Global Burden of Disease Study. *Lancet* 1997; 349: 1498-1504.

[7]   Madison, J. M., Irwin, R. S. Chronic obstructive pulmonary disease. *Lancet* 1998; 352: 467-473.

[8]   Hirayama, F., Lee, A. H., Binns, C. W. Dietary factors for chronic obstructive pulmonary disease: A review of epidemiological evidence. *Expert Rev. Resp. Med.* 2008; 2: 645-653.

[9]   Grievink, L., Smit, H. A., Ocke, M. C., van 't Veer, P., Kromhout, D. Dietary intake of antioxidant (pro)-vitamins, respiratory symptoms and pulmonary function: the MORGEN study. *Thorax* 1998; 53: 166-171.

[10]   Tabak, C., Smit, H. A., Rasanen, L., Fidanza, F., Menotti, A., Nissinen, A., Feskens, E. J., Heederik, D., Kromhout, D. Dietary factors and pulmonary function: a cross sectional study in middle aged men from three European countries. *Thorax* 1999; 54: 1021-1026.

[11]   Hirayama, F., Lee, A. H., Hiramatsu, N. Dietary nutrients in relation to chronic obstructive pulmonary disease: Emerging epidemiological evidence. *Curr. Respir. Med. Rev.* 2010; 6: 124-132.

[12]   Hirayama, F, Lee, A. H., Binns, C. W., Zhao, Y., Hiramatsu, T., Tanikawa, Y., Nishimura, K., Taniguchi, H. Do vegetables and fruits reduce the risk of chronic obstructive pulmonary disease? A case-control study in Japan. *Prev. Med.* 2009; 49: 184-189.

[13]   Tabak, C., Feskens, E. J., Heederik, D., Kromhout, D., Menotti, A., Blackburn, H. W. Fruit and fish consumption: a possible explanation for population differences in COPD mortality (The Seven Countries Study). *Eur. J. Clin. Nutr.* 1998; 52: 819-825.

[14]   Walda, I. C., Tabak, C., Smit, H. A., Rasanen, L., Fidanza, F., Menotti, A., Nissinen, A., Feskens, E. J., Kromhout, D. Diet and 20-year chronic obstructive pulmonary disease mortality in middle-aged men from three European countries. *Eur. J. Clin. Nutr.* 2002; 56: 638-643.

[15] Rautalahti, M., Virtamo, J., Haukka, J., Heinonen, O. P., Sundvall, J., Albanes, D., Huttunen, J. K. The effect of alpha-tocopherol and beta-carotene supplementation on COPD symptoms. *Am. J. Respir. Crit. Care Med.* 1997; 156: 1447-1452.

[16] Smit, H. A. Chronic obstructive pulmonary disease, asthma and protective effects of food intake: from hypothesis to evidence? *Respir. Res.* 2001; 2: 261-264.

INDEX

D

N

O

W

Washington, 24, 25, 32, 77, 79
water, 53, 61, 64, 71, 72, 76, 84, 85, 86, 87, 88
weight loss, 34, 41
wheeze, 101, 103
whole body metabolic regulation, vii, 1

X

xerophthalmia, viii, 59, 61, 68

Y

young adults, 18, 32, 33
Yugoslavia, 101, 103

Z

zeaxanthin, ix, 3, 13, 60, 67, 73
zinc, 17